Contents

Introduction

The purpose of this book is an attempt to get you to examine multiculturalism in a meaningful way. What exactly does the term mean? The first section of the book offers reflections on the topic by some Canadians. They have tried to define multiculturalism by showing how, through our differences, we, in fact, have a universality of experience. Humanity is the tie that binds us to each other.

Each of us is unique. Our experiences and backgrounds are unique as well. Difference is what makes us individual. It is what gives us our identity. The fabric of a country can be enriched by the myriad threads that make up its people. The second section of the book attempts to show our individuality. But it also shows that we are, in fact, no different from each other in many ways.

The story of Canada is a story of challenge and success. For many Canadians the struggle for acceptance and understanding has not been easy. The battle to find a place in society has, at times, been painful. But it has also, at times, been rewarding and fulfilling. The selections in the third section of the book reflect this reality.

Naturally, as we develop a greater sense of our ability to exist in harmony, both acceptance and understanding will evolve. The final section of the book provides some insights into how our individual identities have enriched our own lives and the lives of others. It paints a portrait of relationships which, although having suffered some strain and tension in the making, show the truly unique perspective from which we can view life.

A clear glass window lets in the light. But a stained glass window presents a richness and variety of colour and light which literally makes the ordinary pane pale by comparison. Perhaps if we see multiculturalism as a stained glass window, at least then we can begin to discover the richness and variety we, as Canadians, are fortunate to experience. Perhaps.

Jerry Wowk and Ted Jason

A Multicultural Nation

◆ ◆ ◆

BY WINSTON LOUI

What does it mean to be a Canadian? Does an official document make one "Canadian"? I have often wondered why people question their own identity and why I need to question my own.

Fifteen years ago, I arrived in Toronto with my family. It was a cool summer evening. I felt a chilling freshness in the air; it was different from the warmth of my tropical island home town in Trinidad. In the days that followed, I busily observed the wonders of the big city. But, everywhere I went, eyes stared at me, or so it seemed. Was it the colour of my skin or was it my accented English? I was intimidated by these thoughts. I did not want to brave the new any more. For some time, I only wanted to stand quietly and observe. Fortunately, I began to discover people's friendly natures. They showed interest in my background. They even offered their friendship.

In the meantime, I still had doubts about fitting into Canadian society. But I was determined to establish myself (prove my existence) in some way. I felt impelled to follow what "Canadians" did. Yet somehow, I was not comfortable doing that. It was then that I realized that the Canadian culture is a blend of the cultures and the traditions of the different people living in Canada.

To be Canadian, I simply have to be myself. If I cannot accept myself or appreciate others, how can I expect to live in this multicultural nation? To make my life in Canada worthwhile, I must share my unique heritage.

Today I do not question myself. Canada is my home. And, certainly, I do not have to label myself with a sign that says, "I am Canadian." Why should I? After all, I am one of those different people living in Canada — a Canadian.

Wall

BY

ADAM KOZAKIEWICZ

Grade 9,

Louis St. Laurent High School

Trash for you or anybody else.
A piece of printed paper,
Slightly crumbled edges.
In a blue plastic folder,
Crude and cheap.
Airports, baggage and thousands of miles
Stamped in it.

It is the knife which slit my life in half
The past on one side of the print—Warsaw.
Acacia trees sweet in bloom next
The gray old house damaged in the War
The ancient stone church alive with golden angels.
My friend on his bike
Little black dog.
The drab high-rise building
Which was my loving cradle.
I see, I hear my past from behind
The cruel wall built by this scrap of paper
Cowardly hiding in plastic.
I hurt.

The other side of the print—my present
beauty of white-golden prairies near
Montana border.
Lonely as I,
The mountain amidst the brown hills
Emerald Lake embracing an island.
Silence.
A smile of God in a sunset and in
                              a pillar
of shimmering northern light
descending on a house.

Your smile. Your understanding.

Can the wall turn into a bridge?

4

Smile!

♦ ♦ ♦

BY

KIT

WONG

"S"mile!" said the genial voice of Uncle Ching, who had his camera glued to his left eye. Hang Chan's jaw felt very sore. He had been taking photographs with his relatives for the past half hour. Despite that, he still had to squeeze out another reluctant smile.

Indeed, it should have been a happy day for Hang Chan. It was the day he had longed for all these years. His university graduation ceremony had just been completed a minute ago. Now he was standing on the big lawn in front of Convocation Hall with his academic gown on and his graduation diploma gripped firmly in his hand. Even the weather fit the happy mood of the day. It was the first sunny day after many days of drizzle.

"Now it is Aunt Jade's turn," said Uncle Ching, the geniality and zeal in his tone still unchanged.

"Cut out this picture-taking nonsense! I'm fed up with it!" Hang Chan wanted to yell out loud. But he did not. Instead he walked quietly to stand beside the slight figure of Aunt Jade, put his exhausted arm limply around her shoulder, and manoeuvred his stiffened lips to form a smile, or something close to one. He knew well enough that it was his obligation to pose for pictures. It is the way of the Chinese.

Never in his life did Hang Chan know he had so many relatives. His parents had been busy making phone calls all that week, inviting relatives, even the most remotely related, to his graduation. All this was understandable. After all, what would be a more worthy reason for a pair of Chinese parents to be proud than to have a son who was a university graduate? It has been the Chinese way for a very, very long time.

So it turned out he had to usher about forty people into the hall like a parade before the ceremony had begun. He knew they were really impressed by what they were seeing, for they kept making loud comments in the hall from the minute they entered. All the people were staring at this noisy procession as his relatives seated themselves; however, they were unaware of their conspicuousness, and were still talking loudly. All the solemnity in the hall was swept away. Hang Chan could do nothing but blush. Chinese are not supposed to criticize elder relatives and certainly not to tell them to shut up.

Hang Chan was so lost in his memory of the ceremony that it took him five seconds to realize there was a hand on his shoulder. He turned his head quickly and saw the familiar face of Professor Hoffman, his professor in Chemical Engineering.

"Congratulations, Hang!" said Professor Hoffman heartily. "I can see you have brought your whole family along."

Heavens, who would not see it, Hang thought to himself.

"I never knew you had such a nice family. I even thought you did not have one because you never talked to me about it at all. Why are you keeping them a secret?" asked Professor Hoffman half-jokingly.

Hang Chan's reply was an embarrassed smile. Suddenly, he remembered he had to introduce his parents to Professor Hoffman, according to the unwritten Chinese doctrine or custom.

"This is my father." Hang pointed to a man in his early fifties, fat, with a double chin, wearing a tie so obsolete that it could only be found in movies of Charlie Chaplin's time.

"It is easy to tell with all these resemblances," commented Professor Hoffman good-humouredly.

"And this is my mother."

Professor Hoffman saw a woman quite a few inches shorter than he was, grinning shyly at him like a frightened kid.

"Would you and your parents care to dine with my family tonight? My wife would be most delighted to have you as our guests. Why? You will know if you come tonight." Professor Hoffman winked at Hang Chan after he finished the last sentence and smiled mischievously.

Uncle Ching had been following the conversation all along. He uttered a rapid-fire translation to Hang Chan's parents. They nodded without a moment of hesitation. It is an honour, according to the unwritten doctrine, to dine with a well-educated man, even though Professor Hoffman's manner was quite different from their image of a well-educated man. Impressed by Uncle Ching's ability to translate English, Professor Hoffman also invited him to dinner.

What Hang Chan dreaded most before the graduation had come true. Professor Hoffman had become more than just a teacher to Hang Chan through these years in university. In fact, he and Hang Chan were good friends. Hang Chan had done exceptionally well among his classmates, and Professor Hoffman always said he would like to see the family from which such a brilliant, well-bred student sprang. Now all Professor Hoffman's images of him and his family were going to be shattered because he would see what kind of parents Hang Chan had. Hang Chan's father was a cook who owned a small restaurant in Chinatown. His education had ended in Grade 6 when he had to go to work in order to support his family. After being in Canada for 15 years, he managed to learn to speak English, in the typical Chinese way—very awkwardly and without all the end sounds. His mother was even worse, for she knew no English at all. She had never gone to school and at a very young age had married Hang's father. Because she was always shy in front of strangers, she worked only in the kitchen of their restaurant.

"What am I going to do?" he asked himself as he drove his parents and Uncle Ching to Professor Hoffman's house. A memory of the past flashed back into Hang Chan's mind. It was of the time when he first came to Canada. He had gone to a high school in which he was the only Oriental. He remembered the jeering laughter and whispers of people when he passed by in the hallway. He was so lonely that he studied all the time and got very good marks. People started to accept him and make friends with him. Then Uncle Ching and his family immigrated to Canada. Naturally, his cousin clung to him all the time because he knew the school better. His cousin could speak very little English, and so he was always lost in classes. Hang Chan had to speak Chinese in order to explain things to him. Hang Chan could never forget the staring eyes that turned to him when people heard him speaking Chinese, eyes that seemed as if they were seeing creatures belonging to another species. Hang was eager to make friends, but the segregation between him and other students widened more and more. The same questions went round and round in his head. "Why am I Chinese? Why can't I be a totally Canadian Canadian? And what can I do? Change the colour of my skin?"

From then on, Hang Chan always tried his best to cast away all the Chinese ways so that he could be more Canadian. However, every time he saw the grey hair of his father grow whiter or the wrinkles at the corner of his mother's eyes become deeper, he knew he could not do that. He did not want his relatives to look down on him as a traitor to Chinese customs and thus a disgrace to his family. He was caught in a struggle to find balance between his identity as a Canadian and a Chinese.

Hang Chan was forced back from his thoughts when he realized they had arrived at Professor Hoffman's home. He quickly stepped on the brake and parked the car.

As they entered, Mrs. Hoffman was busy setting the table. Hang Chan's heart started to beat vigorously and his palms were full of sweat. He had given his parents a one-hour lecture on Western table manners, but they had seemed uninterested.

The main course of the meal turned out to be rice and chicken wings. Obviously Mrs. Hoffman intended to suit the tastes of her guests, and her Chinese cooking was not bad. "My wife always said her Chinese food is as good as in a Chinatown restaurant. That is why I invited you all to verify the truth," Professor Hoffman said, smiling.

"I have always liked Chinese cuisine but I could never do it well. So maybe I could get some lessons from Mr. and Mrs. Chan," said Mrs. Hoffman. The spitfire translation of Uncle Ching followed.

Hang's parents said they would be most honoured to help Mrs. Hoffman with her Chinese cooking. Uncle Ching translated. Then the Hoffmans turned their attention to Uncle Ching. They were amazed to learn that Uncle Ching never went to learn English in school. Uncle Ching had come from China just eight years ago, and he knew no English then. His determination enabled him to speak and read English fluently now.

After dinner, Hang's mother tried to pick up the dishes to wash them in the kitchen. Hang stopped her immediately.

"This is not our restaurant, Mother!"

Hang's mother was so nervous that she dropped the dishes, which crashed into pieces on the floor.

Hang Chan was frozen with shame. He thought he was going to lose Professor Hoffman as a friend, as he had lost all his friends in high school. It was then that Professor Hoffman took him out to the terrace. "I notice you have not been very comfortable at the dinner table. I know the reason. You are ashamed of your own culture. I noticed it back at the university. You think people will look down on you because of your ties to your culture."

"But people *do* look down on me because I am Chinese."

"Only those people who do not understand the spirit of Canada do. They think Canadian culture has been invaded by outsiders. What they do not know is that Canadian culture is a mixture of many cultures. Canada has had a long history of accepting immigrants who brought into this vast country many different cultures. Every one of these contributes to the Canadian culture. Thus is formed the multiculturalism of Canada. Have you ever seen the stained glass in a church? Is it not much more beautiful than just plain glass?"

Hang Chan was thinking as he walked back into the kitchen. He found the broken pieces of the dishes were gone already. He saw his father teaching Mrs. Hoffman how to carve a carrot into a rose. Hang's father, like a conjurer, skilfully cut pieces of the carrot, and all of a sudden, there was a rose staring right at everybody. Hang Chan fully understood Hoffman's speech now. There is unique beauty in every culture, and so even though they are different, they can be put together like a mosaic of colourful pieces of glass. He had never seen beauty in his own culture because he was so busy trying to belong to the new culture.

Later on, Hang's mother went to do some knitting with Mrs. Hoffman. They showed each other in turn some special patterns they had created. Uncle Ching got no chance to exercise his spitfire translation skill because the two ladies got on well by themselves. So he went to join Hang Chan, his father, and Professor Hoffman to watch the hockey game on TV.

At nine-thirty the Chan family left. At the door, Hang Chan's mother said the only English phrase she knew to the Hoffmans: "Thank you."

And the Hoffmans understood all the underlying meanings hidden in the words. After all, people do not communicate only by words.

I am a Canadian

◆ ◆ ◆

BY

DUKE

REDBIRD

I'm a lobster fisherman in Newfoundland
I'm a clambake in P.E.I.
I'm a picnic, I'm a banquet
I'm mother's homemade pie
I'm a few drafts in a Legion hall in Fredericton
I'm a kite-flyer in a field in Moncton
I'm a nap on the porch after a hard day's work is
    done.
I'm a snowball fight in Truro, Nova Scotia
I'm small kids playing jacks and skipping rope
I'm a mother who lost a son in the last great war
And I'm a bride with a brand new ring
And a chest of hope
I'm an Easterner
I'm a Westerner
I'm from the North
And I'm from the South
I've swam in two big oceans
And I've loved them both
I'm a clown in Quebec during carnival
I'm a mass in the Cathedral of St. Paul
I'm a hockey game in the Forum
I'm Rocket Richard and Jean Beliveau
I'm a coach for little league Expos
I'm a baby-sitter for sleep-defying rascals
I'm a canoe trip down the Ottawa
I'm a holiday on the Trent

I'm a mortgage, I'm a loan
I'm last week's unpaid rent
I'm Yorkville after dark
I'm a walk in the park
I'm a Winnipeg gold-eye
I'm a hand-made trout fly
I'm a wheat-field and a sunset
Under a prairie-sky
I'm Sir John A. Macdonald
I'm Alexander Graham Bell
I'm a pow-wow dancer
And I'm Louis Riel
I'm the Calgary Stampede
I'm a feathered Sarcee
I'm Edmonton at night
I'm a bar-room fight
I'm a rigger, I'm a cat
I'm a ten-gallon hat
And an unnamed mountain in the interior of B.C.
I'm a maple tree and a totem pole
I'm sunshine showers
And fresh-cut flowers
I'm a ferry boat ride to the Island
I'm the Yukon
I'm the Northwest Territories
I'm the Arctic Ocean and the Beaufort Sea
I'm the prairies, I'm the Great Lakes,
I'm the Rockies, I'm the Laurentians,
I am French
I am English
And I am Métis
But more than this
Above all this
I am a Canadian and proud to be free.

The Profile
of Africa

♦ ♦ ♦

BY

MAXINE

TYNES

We wear our skin like a fine fabric
we people of colour
brown black tan coffee coffee cream ebony
beautiful, strong, exotic in profile
flowering lips
silhouette obsidian planes, curves, structure
like a many-shaded mosaic
we wear our skin like a flag
we share our colour like a blanket
we cast our skin like a shadow
we wear our skin like a map
chart my beginning by my colour
chart my beginning by my profile
read the map of my heritage in
my face
my skin
the dark flash of eye
the profile of Africa.

Palumello

◆ ◆ ◆

B Y

D O N N A

C A R U S O

O n her dresser, the vigil light flickered in front of the picture of Mother Cabrini. I stood on tip toe and inhaled the holy scent of the beeswax candle carefully, so as not to disturb the flame with my breath. I dipped my finger into the warm, melted wax and lifted it up into the cool air to watch it cloud over and harden into a perfect veil — not unlike the one Mother Cabrini wore in her picture, not unlike what women wore in church.

It was long ago, when I was only a girl, and my grandmother, Michelina, was living in my parents' house. I heard her call:

"Dona Maria, veni ca."

Donna Marie, come here.

"Va dormi, va dormi, Dona Marie!"

Go to sleep, go to sleep.

My grandmother would sit on the couch in the afternoon, and I would lie next to her with my head on her lap. I was three. I myself spoke no Italian, her only tongue. But somehow I could understand her every word. She told me of Mother Cabrini's miracles, ones she had witnessed herself.

Like the time an overpowering smell of roses filled the house all day long, when there was in fact only one rose in the house. A blood red one, in front of Mother Cabrini's picture. It was the middle of winter. The same day the letter from Italy came telling my grandma of her mother's death. She knew from the smell of the roses that her mother was with Mother Cabrini in heaven. It was a sign. It kept her heart from breaking.

"Nona, nona," she sang, "filia mia va dormi."

Her lullaby for me. She would ever so gently rock her legs back and forth, singing and singing, until the world fell away and I was sound asleep.

Outdoor sounds, breeze.

Outdoors in summer, she would sit in the sunshine, in her hand a glass sugar jar, an inch of sugar in the bottom. I would be over on the grass watching the bees dancing on the flower tops.

"Dona Maria, veni ca."

A butterfly would light on the sugar, and she would slip the lid onto the jar, then hold it in the sunlight for me to see. We would look at the creature in awe, see it shimmering and happy, then free again, fluttering off, like a houseguest after Sunday dinner warm with love and food.

"Palumello... "

"Butterfly," she would sing...

"Semper vole... "

Always flying...

"Gope bracha de nina mia... "

Now on the arms of my baby...

"A ciell' achendere... "

Up into the sky...

"Quandi mauro... "

When I die...

"Paluma mia, paluma mia, Io 'scende con te."

My butterfly, my butterfly, I'll fly with you.

The sound of "Santa Lucia" on a concertina.

There was an old photograph she had, formal and posed. In it, she stood next to a small man. She was straighter than he; taller. They looked ahead, separate, unsmiling. It was taken on their wedding anniversary.

She held the photograph for me to see as we sat on the couch, the streams of afternoon sunlight making my eyelids heavy with sleep. Again and again she would look from the photo off into space, to the world of her memories, then back again. The story was there in the photo, and there in her sighs. It was a private story, full of love and hope, of disappointment and pain. Full of too many things for a little girl to understand.

Back in my actual time with her, when she gently stroked my hair and coaxed me to sleep, all I understood was, "This was your grandpa. He died before you were born." But later, many years later, after she too was gone, I was haunted by her story, silent yet indelible, written on the walls of my memory.

The sound of a boxing match on TV.

In the evening every Friday, she watched the fights on TV as religiously as she tended the vigil light before Mother Cabrini's picture in her room.

I sat beside her on the couch.

The TV picture was black and white in those days, the men black and white as well. Such fascinating men, in their fancy underwear, hitting each other week after week. Spitting in their corners, sweating, bleeding — their large feet danced as they circled each other, then charged. Fists connected so squarely, I could feel the pain myself.

As we sat together quietly on the couch, never cheering lest we disturb someone, we spent the hour wide-eyed, captivated by the shirtless men in the box. She may have spoken no English, but she understood the language of the fights, as did I. Grandma and I spoke fluent "Friday Night Fights."

Saturday afternoon there was wrestling. Grandma and I watched that, too. But it was my nap time, so I drifted off to sleep as Wild Man was about to pounce on Red Devil, the midget tag-team about to attack the Giant.

I would eventually go to school, the Catholic school, run by nuns who obviously were as enamoured of the Friday Night Fights and wrestling as my grandmother and I. Anything but shirtless and sweaty, they nonetheless knew the power of a quick right to the jaw and the righteousness of a solid headlock.

My grandmother carried her rosary with her always, just as the nuns did. She would sit for hours fingering the beads, petitioning heaven for who knew what.

"Baggi la groce."

"Kiss the cross," she would entreat me in Italian. "Kiss the cross." I would kiss the metal crucifix, warm with the heat of my grandmother's hands. It was Jesus, the Son of God, she said. I remember wondering if Jesus, Son of God, was ever on the Friday Night Fights.

In the other photograph she had, she sat with her four living children, unbelievably young, standing around her. My own mother barely two. It was taken long ago in the days before candid photography, back when every photo was serious and painfully posed with the children in unfamiliar, stiff clothing and shoes that pinched. No wonder everyone was unsmiling.

There was no man in the picture. It would have been taken in Italy to be sent to Grandpa across the ocean. For he had left his wife and babies in Italy while he worked in the new world, where there was opportunity unlike any other. For twenty years he went back and forth and back and forth across the ocean like a migrating bird, while she was free to raise her children alone.

But she was never angry, not when I knew her.

Each morning she would braid up her waist-length hair into a bun and fasten it with long, dark pins. I would stand by her side as, unhurried, she brushed, then braided. The vigil light before Mother Cabrini's picture felt warm on my face as I watched the ritual. The smell of my grandma's hair cream, mixing with the smell of the wax, created the special aroma of my shrine of my grandmother.

She rarely spoke, so each word became a blessing.

"Io te ho cucinato un po di pastina. Mange! Mange!"

"I made you some pastina," she would say as she put the bowl, filled with pasta stars laced with olive oil, before me. My mother fed me Cheerios. Grandma fed me stars. Surely the woman came from heaven if this is what she gave small children for breakfast.

She herself never ate, except for the occasional broiled lamb chop or bowl of homemade soup or piece of fresh fruit. While I ate my pastina, she would stand looking out the window. We were on the second floor, over my parents' grocery store. The kitchen faced the backyard, where there were large fruit trees and rows of my father's lush rosebushes. Birds rested on the telephone wires and paused in their flight across the huge, blue sky. Bees danced on the yellow heads of the dandelions.

We would go out onto the small, second-storey back porch to hang out the wash after breakfast, and I would smell the clean white sheets as she hung them on the line in the breeze. They would billow, once released, like a ship's sail on the ocean. She had crossed an ocean as blue and as vast as the sky to live here with that small dark man in the photograph. The journey had taken nine long days. She must have wondered if the sails that brought her here would ever take her home.

My grandmother and I would sit together on that small back porch enjoying the morning sunshine, high above the yard, and look out over the neighbourhood. Our laundry sailed above that of the neighbours and made us feel we were far in the lead in an important regatta. Ours was the highest clothesline, the longest clothesline, and easily the most spirited. Where we were headed was less important than that we were sailing.

For when it was hot, I wore nothing but the cast which covered me from my waist to my ankles. It had the colour of the white sheets on the line but nothing of the spirit. My shell for a full year, it was the reason my grandmother spent so much time with me. Unlike the others, who were free to go when they liked, I stayed with her, and she stayed with me. For years. She was the old and foreign one; I, a crippled toddler. We didn't matter to anyone and nobody listened to us but, for one another, day by day, we made life wonderful and mysterious.

Sometimes, the other family members would bring the wild western culture home with a bang. From our usual station, the couch, she and I would watch whatever we could not or would not take part in.

Mambo lessons come to mind.

The music was as hot as the Latin countries from which it had sprung. My parents, my aunts and uncles, and seemingly all of their friends wanted to learn this and other exuberant dances.

The living-room, which usually seemed large enough in the quiet afternoons when just my grandmother and I were there, seemed dangerously inadequate to hold the teeming throng of enthusiastic dancers invading the house every Sunday night with their loud and pulsating music.

The instructor made them pair off and learn new steps for an hour, then left them to practise on their own. These practices were what really cemented the relationship between my grandmother and me.

"Setta ca."

"Sit here," she would entreat me as the dancing began. I was only too happy to oblige her by climbing on the couch beside her and snuggling close.

Neither of us could move too quickly: I because of the heavy, unwieldy plaster cast, and she because of the age in her joints. If it became apparent we were no longer safe on the couch—which usually was clear after someone's circle skirt had spun in our faces, or someone had landed in our laps—then it was no easy task to make it past the dancers. We would tightly hold the other's hand, each of us staggering in our own way. As plodding as the dancers were graceful.

In the safety of my grandmother's room, we would lie down on the bed and watch the flickering of the vigil light. Mother Cabrini's face was always serene no matter what the circumstances. The vigil light a soft, flickering glow contrasting with the fire of music and dance consuming the living-room. Grandma would sing to me:

"Palumello... "

Butterfly...

"Semper vole... "

Always flying...

"Gope bracha de nina mia... "
Now on the arms of my baby...
"A ciell' achendere... "
Up into the sky...
"Quandi mauro... "
When I die...
"Paluma mia, paluma mia, Io 'scende con te... "
My butterfly, my butterfly, I'll fly with you.

I was thirteen when she died, the day of her burial in late December most bitterly cold. We lined up, dozens of us, her descendants, her family, and one by one we were handed a cool long-stemmed, blood-red rose to throw into her grave, atop her coffin.

As I approached the open pit, too cold a place for anything but death, as I was about to throw in my rose, the smell of roses wafted through the frigid air. A smell of roses so strong, I knew it was a sign, a sign she had joined all the other daughters of roses in heaven.

Now, as my own life unfolds, I find I decipher more of hers — the cryptic pictures and sighs rubbed clean and intelligible. Her language, my own.

Obituary

♦ ♦ ♦

BY

MYRON

CHORNEY

Old man Stephanovich sat in the sun on the *prispa* in front of his house. Occasional gusts of the spring wind played with strands of his fine white hair.

The mischievous spring breezes jousted with the wispy smoke, making it puff out now from one end, now from the other, of the blue-black T-pipe chimney which surmounted the "ginger-bread" house. The breezes came sweeping up the little hillock upon which the house very squarely stood; they brushed over the bright green blades of grass like fingers of a giant hand passing through a head of closely cropped hair, then rustled aimlessly through the seared straw of the faded brown *streekha* (thatch) like a grey mouse scampering excitely through crackling bullrushes. Light whiffs of wind sped noisily amidst the newly budded leaves of the great poplar and shook the slender branches of the willows clustered near the house. The breezes scampered heedlessly about the grassy hillock startling the trees and the grass and the *streekha*. Only the gingerbread house and Old Man Stephanovich remained unperturbed.

The house stood as it had done every spring for forty years. Whitewashed and thatched, it fitted into the grassy hill as a yellow-crowned daisy fits into a green meadow. There it stood — a green door chaperoned by two green-framed, four-paned windows set in an expanse of white wall, its whiteness, the weather-beaten, orange-brown *streekha* looking less drab when framed by the blue spring sky, the hard form of the T-pipe chimney momentarily outlined against the fleecy softness of a white cloud, a wisp of blue-gray smoke curling aimlessly towards the heavens. There the house stood: beautiful — and practical. For all around the walls, from the ground up as big as a goose could reach, and higher than a chicken could peck, ran a broad coat of brown clay which could not be scarred as whitewash could by marauding barnyard fowl. Lower still, running right around the house as a protection against the scratching and burrowing of restless cats and dogs was a low mound of earth — the *prispa.*

Old Man Stephanovich sat in the sun on the *prispa* in front of his house as he had done every fine spring day for the past five years. He had his curved pipe in his mouth, his cane lay beside him. He sat on the *prispa,* toil-worn shoulders hunched over, white-crowned head nodding, eyes attentive in his tanned, care-lined face. In his scarred and calloused hands he held a well-worn book. His mighty moustache twitched as he read, moving his lips. Every fine spring day for five years now, ever since he had rented his land and stopped working, Old Man Stephanovich had sat in the sun and read.

He loved to read. He had read the few books at his disposal over and over. Yet as a boy in the old country, he had been unable to read because he had never gone to school.

"I didn't learn to read and write until I was married," he used to say. "It was because a villager laughed when, after our marriage, I was unable to sign the church register, that I swore I would learn to read and write. Oh, how I studied at nights! But it was worth it." When the dam of illiteracy had been broken, the old man's pursuit of knowledge flowed unbounded. Whenever he had time, he read. But whereas formerly he had been able to read only during spare moments, he could now sit in the sun on the *prispa* and read all day.

And when people marvelled at his accomplishments, Old Man Stephanovich would say, *"Scho ya!" "Loch-she spomyanit Shevchenka"* — What of me! Better to speak of Shevchenko, Ukraine's greatest poet. Here was a man! He was a serf, a slave until he was twenty-four, an orphan, whose mother died when he was an infant and whose father had felt the whips of the lord's men, a man who spent twelve of his forty-seven years in prisons and Siberia. Yet this man made himself one of the greatest poets of the Slavonic world.

The old man would bow his head and silently trace meaningless figures in the dust with the end of his cane. Then suddenly he would raise his head. "But how many of our children know of Shevchenko? How many know of the people he stood for? How many know of the people he speaks of? We have come to a country where we have at least found homes and freedom — and our children are forgetting their ancestors who fought and worked for centuries to keep their little pieces of land. They forget that we have a history and a culture. They forget that our broad steppes were the barriers between the hordes of the east and the civilization of western Europe. This country gave us land and homes—we will die without giving it anything.

The old man would ponder in such a vein for days, and always he would eventually turn to his wife and say, "Mary, I am glad our son is not ashamed of his people."

"John is a good son," Mary would say. Her eyes would grow sad. "But it has been a long time since we have seen him."

"Toronto is far, Mary, and lawyers are always so busy. Give him time. He'll come. Besides, he has a family of his own to look after now. The baby must be quite a lad now. Oh, if our grandson were only here! I could tell him many stories." Always, their conversation about their son ended with the old man saying, "Oh, if our grandson were here!"

The children walking past from school often saw Old Man Stephanovich sitting on the *prispa*. Sometimes they stopped to talk to him. Then the old man would give them candy (he always had candy for the children), and he would tell them stories.

Oh, the *kazkih* (stories) the old man knew! He would tell them *kazkih* that none of them had ever heard before — all about *Lys Mikita* (Mikita, the fox) who always outwitted Brisko, the dog. And the story of the cat and the rooster who decided to live together, and how the wily fox kidnapped the rooster, and then how the cat took his fiddle, a mallet, and an embroidered knapsack and went to rescue his friend. Oh, the old man could tell *kazkih!* But the children could not often stay to hear him. Reluctantly they passed by the gate, hurrying, because their parents had ordered them to "come straight home after school." And the old man, watching his youthful friends hurrying by, would shake his head and say, "Oh, if my grandson were here! I could talk to him all day long."

And thus Old Man Stephanovich would sit on the *prispa* and read, and think, and dream. As the sun rose high in the sky and moved across the heavens, so the old man would move along the side of the house till in the evening he reached the west wall where he would sit, watching the sun go down. Sometimes he would sit just watching the sun, and sometimes he would sing.

Old Man Stephanovich loved to sing. When one of his musical moods came upon him, he was transformed. He would throw out his barrel chest. Then his rich, powerful tenor would flow out on the evening air, and neighbours' children two or three miles away would run into their houses calling "Mother, Old Man Stephanovich is singing tonight." And all neighbours agreed that the old man had a splendid voice.

"Ah, you should have heard me when I was young!" the old man would say. "If you had heard the men's choir in our village! We couldn't sing in the village hall for fear the walls would come down. So on Sunday evening we would gather outside to sing. They used to hear us at Sniatyn, six miles away."

The old man would pause for a moment. "Young people don't sing as we used to. Oh, they have good voices. But they don't sing songs of a people. You need more than a good voice to sing a song. You have to have it in here," he would say, tapping his breast. "You have to sing from the heart."

Sometimes the old man would grow sad. "The young people don't sing our songs any more," he would say. "Our songs that tell the history of a people. Songs which are as beautiful as the Ukraine, as impressive as the steppes, as glorious as the Cossacks, and as sad as the lonely maidens they speak of. Songs which the *Kobzars* (the bards) sang for hundreds of years — and they are being forgotten." And neighbours often heard his sigh, "If only my grandson were here! How I would like to teach him our songs!"

There were three songs which Old Man Stephanovich sang with more feeling than any others. When he was happy, he would sing *Oy Pid Hayem Hayem* — a song about young people dancing in the orchard. The powerful tenor voice would flippantly cast the jolly notes into the air to dance and frolic among the hills until worn and exhausted they faded into silence. Then the faces of those who heard him brightened and even the sunset seemed to be cheerier.

But when the old man felt thoughtful and melancholy, the neighbours heard another song. Then the words of Shevchenko, set to music, drifted over the evening air, to tell of the Dnieper roaring and moaning, of elm trees creaking in the wind, and of a moon which appeared and disappeared between ominous clouds like a boat that rises and falls on the waves of a stormy sea.

But it was when Old Man Stephanovich was sad that his song was most moving. It was not often that people heard it, for the old man was seldom sad. But when he was, the words of the ballad of *Stenka Razin* would float hauntingly through the air. The slow-moving words seemed to wander among the hills, sad and lonely, far from their native land, telling of the Cossack Stenka Razin and his painted galleys

Immigrants from the Ukraine, c. 1900

boldly sweeping up the Volga. The haunting notes seemed to echo mournfully along the winding valleys, sobbing out their story of the Persian princess who was thrown overboard by Razin to prevent dissension among the Cossacks. And when the last note died out, the neighbours would look at each other and say, "The Old Man will not sleep easily tonight."

One night Old Man Stephanovich sat on the *prispa* on the west side of the house. His shoulders were thrown back, his head was erect. His rich voice reached for the succeedingly higher notes of *Oy Pid Hayem Hayem*. Alex Harasim, bringing in a pail of water for his wife said, "Old Man Stephanovich sounds happier tonight than I've ever heard him. I wonder what he's so happy about?"

"Haven't you heard?" his wife replied. "His son is coming to visit him with his family. He's expecting him tomorrow."

"It's about time!" muttered Alex. "The Old Man worked for years to put John through the University and the boy hasn't come to see his father even once in nine years."

But Old Man Stephanovich, lying sleepless in his bed, found his thoughts going from his son to his daughter-in-law and always stopping with his grandson. What fun he and the boy would have together! He was eight years old now — old enough to be interested in *kazkih* and tales of the Cossacks and little songs. They might even stay two months! Then he and the boy would get to be real friends — and afterwards wouldn't they just give the mailman something to do! All night he tossed about in his bed. The next day he wandered about restlessly until a car drove into the yard. Excited, he and his wife ran to meet it.

The son, the daughter-in-law, the grandson stepped out of the car. The greetings were those of people long parted — a mixture of joy and tears, sobs and laughter, happiness and anxiety.

"Ah, children," said the old man, "it's so good to see you again after all these years." They shook hands and kissed, then embraced and kissed again.

The little boy stood by, bewildered. The old man turned towards him, arms outstretched, *Vnoochko moya! Khodih do Deeda! Khodih do Deeda sinkoo!"* (My little grandson, Come to your grandfather, my boy!) There were tears in the old man's eyes.

The boy did not move.

"Ne vstydaysia, ditino! Khodih do Deeda!" (Do not be shy, son! Come to your grandfather.)

The boy stood motionless.

Old Man Stephanovich heard his son's voice, hesitatingly confused. "Father, Johnny cannot speak the language. We thought it would be best for him ... "

The old man stood dazed. Slowly he bent down, picked up the boy in his arms, and held him close. For some time he did not speak. Then his eyes brightened and he asked anxiously, "You'll be staying a while — a month, two maybe."

"No Father," the son's wife answered. "We can stay only for a week. John has to be back for a convention in three weeks' time and we promised some friends we'd stop in on the way home."

"Yes, Yes." The very wrinkles seemed to deepen in the old man's face. He sighed, and his voice was gentle. "Come, let us go into the house."

"Yes," echoed his wife, "let us go in."

No one heard Old Man Stephanovich sing all that week. But the next Monday, just as the sun balanced on the evening horizon, the neighbours heard his last song. It was the ballad of Stenka Razin echoing among the hills more sadly and more mournfully than they had ever heard it before. And as the song reached them, some of them felt the wind freshen, and looked into the west to see a host of clouds, brilliantly colored by the setting sun, racing toward them across the deep blue of the sky like Stenka Razin's painted galleys. The wind grew stronger and stronger, and some men thought the Old Man's song died out as the cries of the Persian princess might have done when Razin threw her into the Volga.

Tara's Mother-in-law

♦ ♦ ♦

BY

UMA PARAMESWARAN

What kind of place you've brought me to, son?
Where the windows are always closed
And the front door it is always locked?
And no *rangoli* designs on porch steps
To say please come in?
How can you expect Lakshmi to come, son?
You think she'll care to enter
Where the same air goes round and round?
She "the lotus-seated consort
    of him who reposes
    on the primeval ocean of milk"?
You think they'll bless this food
    three days old
    you store in cans and ice-cupboard?

Son, son, it gives me great joy
to see you so well settled,
children and wife and all
Though my hairs do stand on end
When your wife holds hands with men
And you with other men's wives.
But I am glad, son, I really am
That you are settled good good
And thought to bring me all the way
To see this lovely house and car and all.

But I cannot breathe this stale air
With yesterday's cooking smells
going round and round.
Son, cooking is an everyday thing
Not a Sunday work alone
And son, cooking should smell good
The leaping aromas
    of turmeric and green coriander,
    and mustard seeds popped in hot oil
that flavour food, not stink up the air.

Open the windows, son.

I am too used to the sounds
    of living things;
Of birds in the morning
Of rain and wind at night,
Not the drone of furnace fan
    and hiss of hot blasts
    and whoosh whoosh of washing machine.

Open the windows, son,
And let me go back
    to sun and air
    and sweat and even flies and all
But not this, not this.

The Evening I Met My Grandmother

April 20, 1987

◆ ◆ ◆

BY GITA SCHWARTZ

My grandmother died at the age of 72 in the Treblinka Gas Chamber. Her name was Gita Schwartz.

It was sunset, the beginning of the last two holy days of Passover. The candles shimmered, ushering in the holiday. We talked as the sun set and darkness came. My father and I finished dinner. We sat in his bachelor apartment in Montreal, at the round, wooden veneer table—functional, as were all of his meagre possessions. Yet, he thought himself rich, having come from a time and a place where this much was a lot.

We talked of his family. There were fourteen children—seven boys and seven girls. His mother was Gita and his father was Nechemiah. They were farmers in rural Czechoslovakia—Fonchika, near the Hungarian border. Like all parents, Gita and Nechemiah wanted more for their children and sent Morris, my father, off to Nagy Solosh, the nearest town, to apprentice as a tailor. Indeed, in many different ways, my father was a tailor all his working life. It saved his life, too! But that's a story for another time.

This night we spoke of the brothers and sisters. Of David and Hershel and Soreh. Of Rivkah and Yoillie and Layeh. The family was poor in possessions but rich in hands and hearts. There were many to do the chores before breakfast and help Gita with the meals.

When Nechemiah died, the farm was sold. The unmarried children, still living at home, moved to Michalovse with Gita. There was Morris and Moulu, Golda and Chana and Yoillie. Layeh lived nearby with her husband and Rivkah in the next town. The brothers opened a factory making men's clothing. Soreh went to Belgium to marry, as did her sister Basha before her.

By 1945, the fourteen siblings were reduced to five. Fortunately, Tillu and Himmey were already in America before the war broke out. In Europe, three brothers survived—Itzu,

Deszo and Morris. In fact, when my father finally came back from the camps and the forest, to where his home used to be, Deszo and Itzu thought he was Moulu, their youngest brother. Moulu and Morris looked alike and it was three years since the family had been together.

We spoke quietly by candlelight, there, in Montreal, in 1987, but we were transported back to a time and place that no longer exists. A world that holds my roots that I have never seen, yet feel, even today, with a deep and yearning intensity.

Throughout my childhood I listened to my father's war stories, to his stories about his life before the war. He told me about leaving Czechoslovakia when the Communists came, about going to Israel and how hard life was and eventually coming to Canada. I knew his stories intimately and in great detail. Indeed, I have carried his pain as my pain—a mistake children often make in ignorance and compassion and spend a lifetime undoing.

Yes, I listened well and was a good daughter. But this night, this April 20th, 1987, I asked. We had always talked of the pain of surviving. The dead were a huge, hard lump of unexpressed anguish. They were dark and distant and I needed to name them, to hear of their lives, their

work, their loves and their children. I needed to honour each one of them and grieve for them and own them as people I would have loved and hated and befriended and fought with and gone through life with, happily or not.

That night, by candlelight, transported to a kitchen table in a farm house in rural Czechoslovakia, we talked softly and fondly of each of them. I wrote down their names and what is left of the details of their lives. The eldest sister, Basha, who married a diamond cutter, lived in Belgium and had three children. He didn't know when they perished but knew how. The two youngest sisters, Golda, 16, and Chana, 18, were with Gita when she was herded into the gas chamber.

Recalling his youngest brother Moulu and how they were often mistaken for each other, my father wondered why he had survived at all. Why him and not Moulu? He told me how this question had plagued him for years and years. Why him and not his mother? Why him and not his sisters? Why did he have to live with the pain of surviving? Why? When he married and his first child born, he finally understood. He fathered a daughter and named her Gita. He named her Gita so that the spirit of his mother would live on in this world and enrich it. She had been a pious Jew and a devoted mother and her life had not been in vain. She lives on.

I, too, am Gita Schwartz. Although I never met her, I know my grandmother. She lives on in me and moves me. That night, talking softly with my father, by the candlelight ushering in the holy days, she moved me to transform the ordinary into the magical.

Through her, I reach out and touch my ancestors and feel the thread of life pull me deep into the earth.

Jewish refugee children brought to Canada under the Canadian Jewish Congress "War Orphans" project, 1948

The Jade Peony

♦ ♦ ♦

BY

WAYSON

CHOY

When Grandmama died at 83 our whole household held its breath. She had promised us a sign of her leaving, final proof that her present life had ended well. My parents knew that without any clear sign, our own family fortunes could be altered, threatened. My stepmother looked endlessly into the small, cluttered room the ancient lady had occupied. Nothing was touched; nothing changed. My father, thinking that a sign should appear in Grandmama's garden, looked at the frost-killed shoots and cringed: *no, that could not be it.*

My two older teenage brothers and my sister, Liang, age 14, were embarrassed by my parents' behavior. What would all the white people in Vancouver think of us? We were Canadians now, *Chinese-Canadians,* a hyphenated reality that my parents could never accept. So it seemed, for different reasons, we all held our breath waiting for *something.*

I was eight when she died. For days she had resisted going into the hospital ... *a cold, just a cold ...* and instead gave constant instruction to my stepmother and sister on the boiling of ginseng roots mixed with bitter extract. At night, between wracking coughs and deadly silences, Grandmama had her back and chest rubbed with heated camphor oil and sipped a bluish decoction of an herb called Peacock's Tail. When all these failed to abate her fever, she began to arrange the details of her will. This she did with my father, confessing finally: "I am too stubborn. The only cure for old age is to die."

My father wept to hear this. I stood beside her bed; she turned to me. Her round face looked darker, and the gentleness of her eyes, the thin, arching eyebrows, seemed weary. I brushed the few strands of gray, brittle hair from her face; she managed to smile at me. Being the youngest, I had spent nearly all my time with her and could not imagine that we would ever be parted. Yet when she spoke, and her voice hesitated, cracked, the sombre shadows of her room chilled me. Her wrinkled brow grew wet with fever, and her small body seemed even more diminutive.

"I — I am going to the hospital, Grandson." Her hand reached out for mine. "You know, Little Son, whatever happens I will never leave you." Her palm felt plush and warm, the slender, old fingers boney and firm, so magically strong was her grip that I could not imagine how she could ever part from me. Ever.

Her hands *were* magical. My most vivid memories are of her hands: long, elegant fingers, with impeccable nails, a skein of fine, barely-seen veins, and wrinkled skin like light pine. Those hands were quick when she taught me, at six, simple tricks of juggling, learnt when she was a village girl in Southern Canton; a troupe of actors had stayed on her father's farm. One of them, "tall and pale as the whiteness of petals," fell in love with her, promising to return. In her last years his image came back like a third being in our two lives. He had been magician, acrobat, juggler, and some of the things he taught her she had absorbed and passed on to me through her stories and games. But above all, without realizing it then, her hands conveyed to me the quality of their love.

Most marvellous for me was the quick-witted skill her hands revealed in making windchimes for our birthdays: windchimes in the likeness of her lost friend's only present to her, made of bits of string and scraps, in the centre of which once hung a precious jade peony. This wondrous gift to her broke apart years ago, in China, but Grandmama kept the jade pendant in a tiny red silk envelope, and kept it always in her pocket, until her death.

These were not ordinary, carelessly made chimes, such as those you now find in our Chinatown stores, whose rattling noises drive you mad. But making her special ones caused dissension in our family, and some shame. Each one that she made was created from a treasure trove of glass fragments and castaway costume jewellery, in the same way that her first windchime had been made. The problem for the rest of the family was in the fact that Grandmama looked for these treasures wandering the back alleys of Keefer and Pender Streets, peering into our neighbors' garbage cans, chasing away hungry, nervous cats and shouting curses at them.

"All our friends are laughing at us!" Older Brother Jung said at last to my father, when Grandmama was away having tea at Mrs. Lim's.

"We are not poor," Oldest Brother Kiam declared, "yet she and Sek-Lung poke through those awful things as if—" he shoved me in frustration and I stumbled against my sister, "—they were beggars!"

"She will make Little Brother crazy!" Sister Liang said. Without warning, she punched me sharply in the back; I jumped. "You see, look how *nervous* he is!"

I lifted my foot slightly, enough to swing it back and kick Liang in the shin. She yelled and pulled back her fist to punch me again. Jung made a menacing move towards me.

"Stop this, all of you!" My father shook his head in exasperation. How could he dare tell the Grand Old One, his aging mother, that what was somehow appropriate in a poor village in China, was an abomination here. How could he prevent me, his youngest, from accompanying her? If she went walking into those alley-ways alone she could well be attacked by hoodlums. "She is not a beggar looking for food. She is searching for—for.... "

My stepmother attempted to speak, then fell silent. She, too, seemed perplexed and somewhat ashamed. They all loved Grandmama, but she was *inconvenient,* unsettling.

As for our neighbors, most understood Grandmama to be harmlessly crazy, others that she did indeed make lovely toys but for what purpose? *Why?* they asked, and the stories she told me, of the juggler who smiled at her, flashed in my head.

Finally, by their cutting remarks, the family did exert enough pressure so that Grandmama and I no longer openly announced our expeditions. Instead, she took me with her on "shopping trips," ostensibly for clothes or groceries, while in fact we spent most of our time exploring stranger and more distant neighborhoods, searching for splendid junk: jangling pieces of a vase, cranberry glass fragments embossed with leaves, discarded glass beads from Woolworth necklaces....We would sneak them all home in brown rice sacks, folded into small parcels, and put them under her bed. During the day when the family was away at school or work, we brought them out and washed every item in a large black pot of boiling lye and water, dried them quickly, carefully, and returned them, sparkling, under her bed.

Our greatest excitement occurred when a fire gutted the large Chinese Presbyterian Church, three blocks from our house. Over the still-smoking ruins the next day, Grandmama and I rushed precariously over the blackened beams to pick out the stained glass that glittered in the sunlight. Small figure bent over, wrapped against the autumn cold in a dark blue quilted coat, happily gathering each piece like gold, she became my spiritual playmate: "There's a good one! *There!*"

Hours later, soot-covered and smelling of smoke, we came home with a Safeway carton full of delicate fragments, still early enough to steal them all into the house and put the small box under her bed. "These are special pieces," she said, giving the box a last push, "because they come from a sacred place." She slowly got up and I saw, for the first time, her hand begin to shake. But then, in her joy, she embraced me. Both of our hearts were racing, as if we were two dreamers. I buried my face in her blue quilt, and for a moment, the whole world seemed silent.

"My juggler," she said, "he never came back to me from Honan... perhaps the famine...." Her voice began to quake. "But I shall have my sacred windchime...I shall have it again."

One evening, when the family was gathered in their usual places in the parlor, Grandmama gave me her secret nod: a slight wink of her eye and a flaring of her nostrils. There was *trouble* in the air. Supper had gone badly, school examinations were due, father had failed to meet an editorial deadline at the *Vancouver Chinese Times*. A huge sigh came from Sister Liang.

"But it is useless this Chinese they teach you!" she lamented, turning to Stepmother for support. Silence. Liang frowned, dejected, and went back to her Chinese book, bending the covers back.

"Father," Oldest Brother Kiam began, waving his bamboo brush in the air, "you must realize that this Mandarin only confuses us. We are Cantonese speakers...."

"And you do not complain about Latin, French or German in your English school?" Father rattled his newspaper, signal that his patience was ending.

"But, Father, those languages are *scientific,*" Kiam jabbed his brush in the air. "We are now in a scientific, logical world."

Father was silent. We could all hear Grandmama's rocker.

"What about Sek-Lung?" Older Brother Jung pointed angrily at me. "He was sick last year, but this year he should have at least started Chinese school, instead of picking over garbage cans!"

"He starts next year," Father said, in a hard tone that immediately warned everyone to be silent. Liang slammed her book.

Grandmama went on rocking quietly in her chair. She complimented my mother on her knitting, made a remark about the "strong beauty" of Kiam's brushstrokes which, in spite of himself, immensely pleased him. All this babbling noise was her family torn and confused in a strange land: everything here was so very foreign and scientific.

The truth was, I was sorry not to have started school the year before. In my innocence I had imagined going to school meant certain privileges worthy of all my brothers' and sister's complaints. The fact that my lung infection in my fifth and sixth years, mistakenly diagnosed as TB, earned me some reprieve, only made me long for school the more. Each member of the family took turns on Sunday, teaching me or annoying me. But it was the countless hours I spent with Grandmama that were my real education. Tapping me on my head she would say, "Come, Sek-Lung, we have *our* work," and we would walk up the stairs to her small crowded room. There, in the midst of her antique shawls, the old ancestral calligraphy and multi-colored embroidered hangings, beneath the mysterious shelves of sweet herbs and bitter potions, we would continue doing what we had started that morning: the elaborate windchime for her death.

"I can't last forever," she declared, when she let me in on the secret of this one. "It will sing and dance and glitter," her long fingers stretched into the air, pantomiming the waving motion of her ghost chimes; "My spirit will hear its sounds and see its light and return to this house and say goodbye to you."

Deftly she reached into the Safeway carton she had placed on the chair beside me. She picked out a fish-shape amber piece, and with a long needle-like tool and a steel ruler, she scored it. Pressing the blade of a cleaver against the line, with the fingers of her other hand, she lifted up the glass until it cleanly *snapped* into the exact shape she required. Her hand began to tremble, the tips of her fingers to shiver, like rippling water.

"You see that, Little One?" She held her hand up. "That is my body fighting with Death. He is in this room now."

My eyes darted in panic, but Grandmama remained calm, undisturbed, and went on with her work. Then I remembered the glue and uncorked the jar for her. Soon the graceful ritual movements of her hand returned to her, and I became lost in the magic of her task: she dabbed a cabalistic mixture of glue on one end and skillfully dropped the braided end of a silk thread into it. This part always amazed me: the braiding would slowly, *very* slowly, *unknot*, fanning out like a prized fishtail. In a few seconds the clear, homemade glue began to harden as I blew lightly over it, welding to itself each separate silk strand.

Each jam-sized pot of glue was precious; each large cork had been wrapped with a fragment of pink silk. I remember this part vividly, because each cork was treated to a special rite. First we went shopping in the best silk stores in Chinatown for the perfect square of silk she required. It had to be a deep pink, a shade of color blushing toward red. And the tone had to match — as closely as possible — her precious jade carving, the small peony of white and light-red jade, her most lucky possession. In the centre of this semi-translucent carving, no more than an inch wide, was a pool of pink light, its veins swirling out into the petals of the flower.

"This color is the color of my spirit," she said, holding it up to the window so I could see the delicate pastel against the broad strokes of sunlight. She dropped her voice, and I held my breath at the wonder of the color. "This was given to me by the young actor who taught me how to juggle. He had four of them, and each one had a centre of this rare color, the color of Good Fortune." The pendant seemed to pulse as she turned it: "Oh, Sek-Lung! He had white hair and white skin to *his toes! It's true,* I saw him bathing." She laughed and blushed, her eyes softened at the memory. The silk had to match the pink heart of her pendant: the color was magical for her, to hold the unravelling strands of her memory....

It was just six months before she died that we really began to work on her last windchime. Three thin bamboo sticks were steamed and bent into circlets; 30 exact lengths of silk thread, the strongest kind, were cut and braided at both ends and glued to stained glass. Her hands worked on their own command, each hand racing with a life of its own: cutting, snapping, braiding, knotting....Sometimes she breathed heavily and her small body, growing thinner, sagged against me. *Death*, I thought, *He is in this room,* and I would work harder alongside her. For months Grandmama and I did this every other evening, a half dozen pieces each time. The shaking in her hand grew worse, but we said nothing. Finally, after discarding hundreds, she told me she had the necessary 30 pieces. But this time, because it was a sacred chime, I would not be permitted to help her tie it up or have the joy of raising it. "Once tied," she said, holding me against my disappointment, "not even I can raise it. Not a sound must it make until I have died."

"What will happen?"

"Your father will then take the centre braided strand and raise it. He will hang it against my bedroom window so that my ghost may see it, and hear it, and return. I must say goodbye to this world properly or wander in this foreign devil's land forever."

"You can take the streetcar!" I blurted, suddenly shocked that she actually meant to leave me. I thought I could hear the clear-chromatic chimes, see the shimmering colors on the wall: I fell against her and cried, and there in my crying I knew that she would die. I can still remember the touch of her hand on my head, and the smell of her thick woolen sweater pressed against my face. "I will always be with you, Little Sek-Lung, but in a different way...you'll see."

Months went by, and nothing happened. Then one late September evening, when I had just come home from Chinese School, Grandmama was preparing supper when she looked out our kitchen window and saw a cat — a long, lean white cat — jump into our garbage pail and knock it over. She ran out to chase it away, shouting curses at it. She did not have her thick sweater on and when she came back into the house a chill gripped her. She leaned against the door: "That was not a cat," she said, and the odd tone of her caused my father to look with alarm at her. "I can not take back my curses. It is too late." She took hold of my father's arm. "It was all white and had pink eyes like sacred fire."

My father started at this, and they both looked pale. My brothers and sister, clearing the table, froze in their gestures.

"The fog has confused you," Stepmother said. "It was just a cat."

But Grandmama shook her head, for she knew it was a sign. "I will not live forever," she said. "I am prepared."

The next morning she was confined to her bed with a severe cold. Sitting by her, playing with some of my toys, I asked her about the cat: "Why did father jump at the cat with the pink eyes? He didn't see it, you did."

"But he and your mother know what it means."

"What?"

"My friend, the juggler, the magician, was as pale as white jade, and he had pink eyes." I thought she would begin to tell me one of her stories, a tale of enchantment or of a wondrous adventure, but she only paused to swallow; her eyes glittered, lost in memory. She took my hand, gently opening and closing her fingers over it. "Sek-Lung," she sighed, "*he* has come back to me."

Then Grandmama sank back into her pillow and the embroidered flowers lifted to frame her wrinkled face. I saw her hand over my own, and my own began to tremble. I fell fitfully asleep by her side. When I woke up it was dark and her bed was empty. She had been taken to the hospital and I was not permitted to visit.

A few days after that she died of the complications of pneumonia. Immediately after her death my father came home and said nothing to us, but walked up the stairs to her room, pulled aside the drawn lace curtains of her window and lifted the windchimes to the sky.

I began to cry and quickly put my hand in my pocket for a hand-kerchief. Instead, caught between my fingers, was the small, round firmness of the jade peony. In my mind's eye I saw Grandmama smile and heard, softly, the pink centre beat like a beautiful, cramped heart.

I Grew Up

◆ ◆ ◆

BY LENORE KEESHIG-TOBIAS

i grew up on the reserve
thinking it was the most
beautiful place in the world

i grew up thinking
i'm never going
to leave this place

i was a child
a child who would
lie under trees

watching wind's rhythms
sway leafy boughs
back and forth

back and forth
sweeping it seemed
the clouds into great piles

and rocking me as
i snuggled in the grass
like a bug basking in the sun

i grew up on the reserve
thinking it was the most
beautiful place in the world

i grew up thinking
i'm never going
to leave this place

i was a child
a child who ran
wild rhythms

through the fields
the streams
the bush

eating berries
cupping cool water
to my wild stained mouth

and hiding in the
treetops with
my friends

we used to laugh at teachers and
tourists who referred to
our bush as *forests* or *woods*

forests and *woods*
were places of
fairytale text

were places where people
especially children, got lost
where wild beasts roamed

our bush was where we played
and where the rabbits squirrels
foxes deer and the bear lived

i grew up thinking
i'm never going
to leave this place

i grew up on the reserve
thinking it was the most
beautiful place in the world

What Do We Do with a Variation?

♦ ♦ ♦

BY JAMES BERRY

What do we do with a difference?
Do we stand and discuss its oddity
or do we ignore it?

Do we shut our eyes to it
or poke it with a stick?
Do we clobber it to death?

Do we move around it in rage
and enlist the rage of others?
Do we will it to go away?

Do we look at it in awe
or purely in wonderment?
Do we work for it to disappear?

Do we pass it stealthily
or change route away from it?
Do we will it to become like ourselves?

What do we do with a difference?
Do we communicate to it,
let application acknowledge it
for barriers to fall down?

The
Other
Family

♦ ♦ ♦

BY

HIMANI

BANNERJI

When the little girl came home it was already getting dark. The winter twilight had transformed the sheer blue sky of the day into the colour of steel, on which were etched a few stars, the bare winter trees and the dark wedges of the house tops. A few lit windows cast a faint glow on the snow outside. The mother stood at her window and watched the little hooded figure walking toward the house. The child looked like a shadow, her blue coat blended into the shadows of the evening. This child, her own, how small and insubstantial she seemed, and how alone, walking home through a pavement covered with ice and snow! It felt unreal. So different was this childhood from her own, so far away from the sun, the trees and the peopled streets of her own country! What did I do, she thought, I took her away from her own people and her own language, and now here she comes walking along, through an alien street in a country named Canada.

As she contemplated the solitary, moving figure, her own solitude rushed over her like a tide. She had drifted away from a world that she had lived in and understood, and now she stood here at the same distance from her home as from the homes which she glimpsed while walking past the sparkling clean windows of the sandblasted houses. And now the door bell rang, and here was her daughter scraping the snow off her boots on the door mat.

Dinner time was a good time. A time of warmth, of putting hot, steaming food onto the table. A time to chat about the important things of the day, a time to show each other what they had acquired. Sometimes, however, her mother would be absent-minded, worried perhaps about work, unsettled perhaps by letters that had arrived from home, scraping her feelings into a state of rawness. This was such an evening. She had served herself and her child, started a conversation about their two cats and fallen into a silence after a few minutes.

"You aren't listening to me, Mother."

The complaining voice got through to her, and she looked at the indignant face demanding attention from the other side of the table. She gathered herself together.

"So what did he do, when you gave him dried food?"

"Oh, I don't quite remember, I think he scratched the ground near his bowl and left."

The child laughed.

"That was smart of him! So why don't we buy tinned food for them?"

"Maybe we should," she said, and tried to change the topic.

"So what did you do in your school today?"

"Oh, we drew pictures like we do every day. We never study anything—not like you said you did in your school. We drew a family — our family. Want to see it?"

"Sure, and let's go to the living room, OK? This is messy." Scraping of chairs and the lighting of the lamps in the other room. They both made a rush for the most comfortable chair, both reached it at the same time and made a compromise.

"How about you sit in my lap? No? OK, sit next to me then and we will squeeze in somehow."

There was a remarkable resemblance between the two faces, except that the face of the child had a greater intensity, given by the wide open eyes. She was fine boned, and had black hair framing her face. Right now she was struggling with the contents of her satchel, apparently trying to feel her way to the paintings.

"Here it is," she said, producing a piece of paper. "Here's the family!"

The mother looked at the picture for a long time. She was very still. Her face had set into an expression of anger and sadness. She was trying very hard not to cry. She didn't want to frighten the child, and yet what she saw made her feel distant from her daughter, as though she was looking at her through the reverse end of a telescope. She couldn't speak at all. The little girl too sat very still, a little recoiled from the body of her mother, as though expecting a blow. Her hands were clenched into fists, but finally it was she who broke the silence.

"What happened?" she said. "Don't you like it?"

"Listen," said the mother, "this is not your family. I, you and your father are dark-skinned, dark-haired. I don't have a blond wig hidden in my closet, my eyes are black, not blue, and your father's beard is black, not red, and you, do you have a white skin, a button nose with freckles, blue eyes and blond hair tied into a pony tail? You said you drew our family. This is not it, is it?"

The child was now feeling distinctly cornered. At first she was startled and frightened by her mother's response, but now she was prepared to be defiant. She had the greatest authority behind her, and she now summoned it to her help.

"I drew it from a book," she said, "all our books have this same picture of the family. You can go and see it for yourself. And everyone else drew it too. You can ask our teacher tomorrow. She liked it, so there!"

The little girl was clutching at her last straw.

"But you? Where are you in this picture?" demanded her mother, by now thoroughly aroused. "Where are we? Is this the family you would like to have? Don't you want us anymore? You want to be a *mem-sahib,* a white girl?"

But even as she lashed out these questions the mother regretted them. She could see that she made no sense to the child. She could feel the unfairness of it all. She was sorry that she was putting such a heavy burden on such young shoulders.

"First I bring her here," she thought, "and then I try to make her feel guilty for wanting to be the same as the others." But something had taken hold of her this evening. Panic at the thought of losing her child, despair and guilt galvanized her into speech she regretted, and she looked with anger at her only child, who it seemed wanted to be white, who had rejected her dark mother. Someday this child would be ashamed of her, she thought, someday would move out into the world of those others. Someday they would be enemies. Confusing thoughts ran through her head like images on an uncontrollable television screen, in the chaos of which she heard her ultimate justification flung at her by her daughter — they wanted me to draw the family, didn't they? "They" wanted "her" to draw "the family." The way her daughter pronounced the words "they" or "the family" indicated that she knew what she was talking about. The simple pronoun "they" definitely stood for authority, for that uncontrollable yet organized world immediately outside, of which the school was the ultimate expression. It surrounded their own private space. "They" had power, "they" could crush little people like her anytime "they" wanted to, and in "their" world that was the picture of the family. Whether her mother liked it or not, whether she looked like the little girl in it or not, made not one jot of difference. That was, yes, that was the right picture. As these thoughts passed through her mind, her anger ebbed away. Abandoning her fury and distance, the mother bowed her head at the image of this family and burst into sobs.

"What will happen to you?" she said. "What did I do to you?"

She cried a great deal and said many incoherent things. The little girl was patient, quietly absorbing her mother's change of mood. She had a thoughtful look on her face, and bit her nails from time to time. She did not protest any more, but nor did she cry. After a while her mother took her to bed and tucked her in, and sat in the kitchen with the fearful vision of her daughter always outside of the window of the blond family, never the centre of her own life, always rejecting herself, and her life transformed into a gigantic peep show. She wept very bitterly because she had caused this destruction, and because she had hated her child in her own fear of rejection, and because she had sowed guilt into her mind.

When her mother went to bed and closed the door, the child, who had been waiting for long, left the bed. She crossed the corridor on her tiptoes, past the row of shoes, the silent gathering of the overcoats and the mirror with the wavy surface, and went into the washroom. Behind the door was another mirror, of full length, and clear. Deliberately and slowly the child took off the top of her pyjamas and surveyed herself with grave scrutiny. She saw the brownness of her skin, the wide, staring, dark eyes, the black hair now tousled from the pillows, the scar on her nose and the brownish pink of her mouth. She stood a while lost in this act of contemplation, until the sound of soft padded feet neared the door, and a whiskered face peeped in. She stooped and picked up the cat and walked back to her own room.

It was snowing again, and little elves with bright-coloured coats and snow in their boots had reappeared in the classroom. When finally the coats were hung under pegs with names and boots neatly stowed away, the little girl approached her teacher. She had her painting from the day before in her hand.

"I have brought it back," she said.

"Why?" asked the teacher, "don't you like it any more?"

The little girl was looking around very intently.

"It's not finished yet," she said. "The books I looked at didn't have something. Can I finish it now?"

"Go ahead," said the teacher, moving on to get the colours from the cupboard.

The little girl was looking at the classroom. It was full of children of all colours, of all kinds of shapes of noses and of different colours of hair. She sat on the floor, placed the incomplete picture on a big piece of newspaper and started to paint. She worked long at it — and with great concentration. Finally it was finished. She went back to her teacher.

"It's finished now," she said, "I drew the rest."

The teacher reached out for the picture and spread it neatly on a desk. There they were, the blond family arranged in a semicircle with a dip in the middle, but next to them, arranged alike, stood another group — a man, a woman, and a child, but they were dark-skinned, dark-haired, the woman wore clothes from her own country, and the little girl in the middle had a scar on her nose.

"Do you like it?"

"Who are they?" asked the teacher, though she should have known. But the little girl didn't mind answering this question one bit.

"It's the other family," she said.

Should I Change My Name?

♦ ♦ ♦

BY

MATHEYALAGAN

NAGARANTHY

My parents tell me that when I was born, my father looked at me for about half an hour. My mother asked my father, "What's the matter with you? Why are you looking so puzzled?" My father did not hear what she was saying because he was thinking about what to call me. My father said, "My son...No, no, our son! He is very beautiful—like a moon! And very bright—like a sun!" So my parents decided to give me the name Matheyalagan—Mathey means "moon," "beauty," "sun," and "stars." Another meaning is "good," "intelligent," and "brave." Alagan means "beauty."

When I was old enough to learn the meaning of my name, I asked my parents, "Why did you choose this name? It embarrasses me. Could you please change it?"

My mom was angry with me. She said, "Don't ever be ashamed of your name. It will bring you good luck in your life." I remember my mother's advice now. When Canadians get impatient with my name because it is hard to say and it is too long, I remember what my name means, and I never consider changing it.

The Nun
Who Returned to
Ireland

◆ ◆ ◆

BY ROCH CARRIER

After my first day of school I ran back to the house, holding out my reader.

"Mama, I learned how to read!" I announced.

"This is an important day," she replied; " I want your father to be here to see."

We waited for him. I waited as I'd never waited before. And as soon as his step rang out on the floor of the gallery, my first reader was open on my knees and my finger was pointing to the first letter in a short sentence.

"Your son learned to read today," my mother declared through the screen door. She was as excited as I.

"Well, well!" said my father. "Things happen fast nowadays. Pretty soon, son, you'll be able to do like me — read the newspaper upside down in your sleep!"

"Listen to me!" I said.

And I read the sentence I'd learned in school that day, from Sister Brigitte. But instead of picking me up and lifting me in his arms, my father looked at my mother and my mother didn't come and kiss her little boy who'd learned to read so quickly.

"What's going on here?" my father asked.

"I'd say it sounds like English," said my mother, "Show me your book." (She read the sentence I'd learned to decipher.) "I'd say you're reading as if you were English. Start again."

I reread the short sentence.

"You're reading with an English accent!" my mother exclaimed.

"I'm reading the way Sister Brigitte taught me."

"Don't tell me he's learning his own mother tongue in English," my father protested.

I had noticed that Sister Brigitte didn't speak the way we did, but that was quite natural because we all knew that nuns don't do anything the way other people do; they didn't dress like everybody else, they didn't get married, they didn't have children and they always lived in hiding. But as far as knowing whether Sister Brigitte had an English accent, how could I? I'd never heard a single word of English.

Over the next few days I learned that she hadn't been born in our village; it seemed very strange that someone could live in the village without being born there, because everyone else in the village had been born in the village.

Our parents weren't very pleased that their children were learning to read their mother tongue with an English accent. In whispers, they started to say that Sister Brigitte was Irish — that she hadn't even been born in Canada. Monsieur Cassidy, the undertaker, was Irish too, but he'd been born in the village, while Sister Brigitte had come from Ireland.

"Where's Ireland?" I asked my mother.

"It's a very small, very green little country in the ocean, far, far away."

As our reading lessons proceeded I took pains to pronounce the vowels as Sister Brigitte did, to emphasize the same syllables as she; I was so impatient to read the books my uncles brought back from their far-off colleges. Suddenly it was important for me to know.

"Sister Brigitte, where's Ireland?"

She put down her book.

"Ireland is the country where my parents were born, and my grandparents and my great-grandparents. And I was born in Ireland too. I was a little girl in Ireland. When I was a child like you I lived in Ireland. We had horses and sheep. Then the Lord asked me to become his servant..."

"What does that mean?"

"The Lord asked me if I wanted to become a nun. I said yes. So then I left my family and I forgot Ireland and my village."

"Forgot your village?"

I could see in her eyes that she didn't want to answer my question.

"Ever since, I've been teaching young children. Some of the children who were your age when I taught them are grandparents now, old grandparents."

Sister Brigitte's face, surrounded by her starched coif, had no age; I learned that she was old, very old, because she had been a teacher to grandparents.

"Have you ever gone back to Ireland?"

"God didn't want to send me back."

"You must miss your country."

"God asked me to teach little children to read and write so every child could read the great book of life."

"Sister Brigitte, you're older than our grandparents! Will you go back to Ireland before you die?"

The old nun must have known from my expression that death was so remote for me I could speak of it quite innocently, as I would speak of the grass or the sky. She said simply:

"Let's go on with our reading. School children in Ireland aren't as disorderly as you."

All that autumn we applied ourselves to our reading; by December we could read the brief texts Sister Brigitte wrote on the blackboard herself, in a pious script we tried awkwardly to imitate; in every text the word Ireland always appeared. It was by writing the word Ireland that I learned to form a capital I.

After Christmas holidays Sister Brigitte wasn't at the classroom door to greet us; she was sick. From our parents' whispers we learned that Sister Brigitte had lost her memory. We weren't surprised. We knew that old people always lose their memories and Sister Brigitte was an old person because she had been a teacher to grandparents.

Late in January, the nuns in the convent discovered that Sister Brigitte had left her room. They looked everywhere for her, in all the rooms and all the classrooms. Outside, a storm was blowing gusts of snow and wind; you couldn't see Heaven or earth, as they said. Sister Brigitte, who had spent the last few weeks in her bed, had fled into the storm. Some men from the village spotted her black form in the blizzard; beneath her vast mantle she was barefoot. When the men asked her where she was going, Sister Brigitte replied in English that she was going home, to Ireland.

Our Subdivision

♦ ♦ ♦

BY

NIGEL

DARBASIE

Perfunctory greetings
exchanged in winter
while shovelling snow
from driveways and sidewalks.

Summer weekend conversations
curtailed: wash our cars
mow our lawns
apply weed & feed
to grow healthy grass
and kill the dandelions.

Words set down
as wood and wire fences
fixing distance
preserving our immigrant
separateness
in every season of discourse.

Equal Opportunity

◆ ◆ ◆

BY

JIM WONG-CHU

in early Canada
when railways were highways

each stop brought new opportunities

there was a rule

    the chinese could only ride
    the last two cars
    of the trains

that is

until a train derailed
killing all those
in front

(the chinese erected an altar and thanked buddha)

a new rule was made

the chinese must ride
the front two cars
of the trains

that is

until another accident
claimed everyone
in the back

(the chinese erected an altar and thanked buddha)

after much debate
common sense prevailed

the chinese are now allowed
to sit anywhere
on any train

Meeting Jim Crow

◆ ◆ ◆

BY

CHERYL

FOGGO

There was nothing amiss, nothing lacking in Bowness. In 1958, my parents bought a house there for seven thousand dollars. It had no plumbing, no basement, no porch, an unfinished yard and only five small rooms.

Our street, 70th Street, was gravel and dust. No street lamps. No trees. When the wind blew, which it did frequently, great clouds of sand would whirl up and spin across the road. My brothers and sister and I, and our friends, were delighted by these dust storms. Someone would shriek, "It's a tornado!" and we would chase the cloud, madly laughing.

Around the corner and up 46th Avenue was a cluster of businesses—the bakery, the hardware store, Gibson's Variety, a cafe, the library and the Crystal Grocery, which everyone referred to as "Garry's," after the proprietor, Garry Fong.

At the other end of 70th Street was Bowcroft Elementary which my brothers attended, and the kindergarten which I attended in the basement of the United Church. Before gaining the church doors, there was a long, wide, grassy field to master. Initially, the crossing of this field required a certain amount of courage-gathering. The grass was, in places, as tall as I, and the boulders in the distance might have provided cover for an animal or a bully. Soon, though, bolstered by the company of my friend Ricky Hayes, the field's gently waving rainbow-colored foxtails became a treasured part of the enjoyment in a five-year-old life.

Our street contained the closest thing to a Black community that one would find in Calgary in 1961. Ricky Hayes' parents were biracial, but he, his brother Randy and sister Debbie considered themselves Black. The Hayes', their grandparents across the alley, my family and the Saunders and Lawson families up the road comprised what I believe was the largest concentration of Black people in a single Calgary neighborhood.

My parents had an attitude of kinship toward the other Black families on the street. The families knew one another, they knew each other's parents and grandparents, and probably because of that "knowing," they communicated to us our connection to other Black children. We played together. Without isolating ourselves from the other children in the neighborhood and without any discussion of it, we sensed a link that transcended our environs.

Across the street from our house was another field which we had to cross to reach the railroad tracks leading to the twin bridges, the Bow River, and ultimately, to the paths that took us "up in the hills."

Most summer days we spent meandering along the tracks to the river, the usual goal being a picnic in the hills. The picnic, however, was not really the point. The point was the adventure we would sometimes encounter along the way.

On a very warm day, if there was no breeze, the heat from the iron rails and sharp smell of oil and metal bouncing up into our faces would drive us down from the tracks to walk through the high grasses. This meant slower going, but it was good to sniff the flowers instead of the heat and to dig around what someone would insist was a badger hole.

From the first time my brothers pronounced me old enough to go along with them, until I was sixteen and we moved from Bowness, the journey along the tracks to the river, across the bridges and up into the hills was real life. It was the meeting place, it was where we went to talk and light campfires, it was something we did that our parents did not do.

Across the alley from us lived two children, a brother and sister, who never joined the treks to the hills if we and the Hayes children were going. Their father forbade them from associating with us, and effectively ostracized his children from the rest of the neighborhood by prohibiting them from joining any games where we Black children were present. When groups formed for kick-the-can or softball, we were often aware of these two children's eyes peering out from the cracks in their fence. They were there, we were aware of their presence, and in retrospect, their loneliness seems palpable.

When I was young, I was minimally aware that racism was a special problem. People who shared our neighbor's prejudices seemed so rare and to have so little effect on my life that I did not attribute their bigotry to a world condition.

My mother had implanted in the

minds of my two older brothers, my younger sister and myself that we were special, not ordinary in any way. She would refer to our bigoted neighbor with utter contempt, as "the likes of him," implying that his ideas and his two unfortunate children were unworthy of our time or thoughts.

The diligence of our mother freed the minds of me and my siblings from the self-hatred that can cripple Black children born in ghettos.

Still, even a fiercely proud mother's constant reassurances cannot protect her Black child from learning, sooner or later, that skin is a badge you will always wear, a form of identification for those in the world who wish to brand you.

One afternoon upon returning from school I overheard my mother talking on the telephone to Mr. Leavitt, the principal of my elementary school. He was calling to plead with her to try to persuade Floyd Hayes to discourage his children from fighting at school. Floyd was the brother of my mother's twin sister's husband and the father of the aforementioned friends, Randy, Ricky and Debbie.

"I'm afraid that I can't agree with you, Mr. Leavitt," she was saying. "I'm not going to tell them how to handle their problems. They came from a place where they can't fight. Where they come from a Black person doesn't have a chance against racists, and if Mr. Hayes has decided his children are going to fight name-calling with their fists, that's up to him."

When my mother replaced the receiver on its hook on the wall, I pestered her with questions. What did Mr. Leavitt want? Why had he called her? Were Randy and Ricky in trouble? What did she mean when she said Floyd had come from somewhere else where they couldn't fight it? Fight what?

"Jim Crow. They couldn't fight Jim Crow down there, but he's determined he's going to fight it here."

"Who is Jim Crow?"

"It's not who, it's what. It's called Jim Crow when Black people aren't allowed to ride at the front of the bus, or drink from the same fountains as Whites."

"Jim Crow?" I repeated. "Jim Crow. Where is the Jim Crow?"

"Kansas. Floyd and them were all born in Kansas."

If Floyd "and them" were all born in Kansas, that meant that my Uncle Allen, Floyd's younger brother, had been born there too, and that he had lived with this Jim Crow.

"Is Kansas in Canada?" I asked nervously.

"No, oh no," my mother said.

"We don't have that kind of thing here. Kansas is in the States. Allen and Floyd and them never went to the movie houses when they were kids, not because they didn't believe in it, but because nobody was going to tell them that they had to sit up in the balcony or at the back. They came to Canada to get away from that, and they figure they're not going to tell their kids to stand by while anyone calls them 'nigger' either."

My mother was clearly quite agitated by Mr. Leavitt's call. I knew that she would repeat the entire conversation, with some embellishment, to her sisters Pearl and Edie on the telephone later that evening.

As for me, I was relieved to learn that Kansas was not in Canada. Here was yet another story, another horrific tale of life in "The States," fuelling my growing belief that I was lucky to have been born in Canada.

Only short days before Mr. Leavitt's call I had learned that my grandparents, my mother's father and mother, had also once lived in America.

The discovery came to me when I asked my mother to explain why my grandpa was White, yet his brother, Uncle Buster, was Black.

My grandfather was something less than five feet, ten inches tall. He had grey eyes, he wore glasses over his long, narrow nose and he was light-skinned.

He had been called George Washington Smith at birth, but upon joining the Canadian Army in 1919 he revealed the full extent of his embarrassment over the name and lied to his commanding officer, saying that his middle initial stood for Willis. Thereafter, he was known as George Willis Smith and that is how I knew him.

I believe he possessed an average build, although it is difficult to be certain as he always dressed in loose clothing, in particular a pair of grey-beige pants and a yellow shirt.

He had a deep voice and a low, rolling, rumbling laugh. He began most sentences with the phrase, "Well, ya take." He called his five sons "Son," his four daughters "Daughter" and he sometimes called me "Granddaughter."

He would say, "Well, ya take, granddaughter, I don't yodel when big girls (referring to my grandmother, who was singing in the kitchen) are listenin'. I only yodel for special small girls."

He was born in Chandler, Oklahoma, on October 31st, 1897. When I say that he was light-skinned, I mean that his skin color was indistinguishable from that of any White person.

That is why, in 1963 when I was seven years old, I asked my mother how he could be White and his brother be Black.

She turned and stared at me. "Your Grandpa is not White."

"He is," I said.

I went to the china cabinet and took the photograph of my grandparents with their children taken on the occasion of their fortieth wedding anniversary. Carefully, I took it to my mother and placed it in her hands.

"Look."

My mother took the picture and brushed it gently, wiping away imaginary dust.

"He has very fair skin, honey, but he isn't a White man. What he would say if he knew his grandchildren thought so!" She was very amused and continued, "You see, just look at his hair."

I looked, but seeing nothing remarkable about his metallic-grey, brushed-back hair, did not speak.

"You're not going to find any White man on earth with hair like that," she said. "Daddy has him some bad hair."

"Bad" was how she described any head of hair, like my brother Richard's or my cousin Sharon's, that was very tight and nappy. She frequently caused me considerable grief by comparing my hair with my sister's, whose loose and supple hair qualified as "good hair."

I continued to gaze glumly at the photograph in my mother's hand. I was embarrassed at having been wrong about my grandfather. There he sat, beside my dark-skinned grandmother, to whom all along I thought he had been blissfully and interracially married.

"Grandma is Black." I finally said.

"Uhhm hmm, no one would ever mistake your grandmother for White. Daddy and Mama used to run into trouble when they went back to the States. If Daddy wears a hat, you see, he can't lay claim to his heritage. He used to wonder why nobody bothered him when he went into the White areas.

"Once, Mama and Daddy went to Oklahoma to see Mom's relatives. They'd been shopping and made plans to meet in a restaurant for lunch. Daddy got there first, took a table and told the waiter that he was waiting for his wife. He didn't take his hat off until he sat down. When Mama got there she joined Daddy at his table, but no one came to take their order. The waiter walked all around them, just like they weren't there. He acted like he was deaf when Daddy said 'Excuse me.'

"Finally a person came from the kitchen and whispered, 'I'm sorry, but we won't be able to serve you today.'

"Daddy was shocked. He was a young boy when they left the

States and had forgotten what it was like there. He really got angry. He stood up and said, 'You sure were planning to serve me before I took my hat off.' He started to go toward the man, but Mama stopped him. 'No George, let's just get our things and go,' she said, 'We don't need for you to land up in jail down here.' Mama and daddy got out of there and shook the dust of that place off of their feet. Daddy's never gone back again, never again."

Knowing my grandparents to be the gentle, lovely people that they were, I couldn't imagine what kind of madness would cause them to be treated in such a manner. I began to fear the very words whenever I heard someone refer to "The States." I vowed that I, like my grandfather, would not bother to darken America's doorstep.

Thinking it over now, it is easy for me to see what would have been the most difficult thing about the Oklahoma experience for my grandfather. To walk away from a man who had insulted his wife by refusing to serve her would have been contrary to his principles. He believed that among his functions, one of his "jobs" was to protect his wife. It was up to him to see that life provided her the ordinary dignities that she deserved.

Following the conversation with my mother that day, I sat down to write my grandparents a letter. I did not mention the story that my mother had told me. I mentioned that I had recently had my tonsils removed, that we would be, as usual, travelling to Winnipeg to see them during the Easter break from school and that I no longer wept when my mother washed my hair.

from

Angel Square

◆ ◆ ◆

BY

BRIAN

DOYLE

That night I went to bed early.

And I tried a prayer.

I had never tried a prayer before.

I prayed for a nice time.

A time when nobody thought some other person's face was funny to look at and nobody laughed at other people's parents and said they were stupid-looking and nobody made fun of the way they talked and nobody thought somebody else wore funny-looking clothes or hateful clothes.

And nobody got beat up because of the kind of hat they wore or because they were poor or because of the street they lived on.

And nobody got spit on because they had different kinds of food in their lunch or their father came to meet them after school with a long coat on and maybe a beard.

And nobody got their mitts stolen or got tripped in the snow because their names didn't sound right or they believed in some other kind of religion or read a different kind of bible or had freckles on their faces or had the wrong kind of hair or had to go home at a different time from school or didn't have skates or *did* have skates or weren't allowed to play alleys on Saturday or on Sunday or *were*, or got dunked in water at church or didn't swear or *did* swear or smelled funny or couldn't eat fish or *had* to eat fish or wore a hat in church or *didn't* wear a hat in church or said the Lord's Prayer different or *didn't* say the Lord's Prayer at all.

And nobody got punched in the mouth because they had clean fingernails or fat lips or couldn't understand English or couldn't speak French or couldn't pronounce Hebrew.

And there were no gangs waiting all the time, so nobody had to go down different streets just to get to the store or go to school.

And you could carry a book along with you or a mouth organ or something and people wouldn't take it from you and then tear it into pieces or grab it and smash it up against a wall.

A time when you maybe liked a girl and they wouldn't come along and twist your arm behind your back and try and make you say dirty things about her.

A nice time.

That's what I prayed for.

The prayer might work, I thought.

Or it might not.

It was a mystery.

from

From Anna

◆ ◆ ◆

B Y

J E A N

L I T T L E

The Second Day

Anna watched her feet walking along.

One…two…one…two…

Soon she would be at the school. Maybe she could even see it now if she looked up. She did not look up.

It was a long walk but there was no way to get lost. You just keep going straight ahead after you got to the first big street and turned left. Mama had watched until Anna had made that first turn safely. So she was not lost.

She felt lost though.

One…two…one…two…

Yesterday at school they had been nice but she was new yesterday. Today she would probably be Awkward Anna again. Miss Williams would not smile.

Today she'll want me to read from a book, Anna told herself, getting ready for the worst.

"Hi, Anna," a boy's voice called.

Anna looked up without stopping to think. The next instant, she felt silly. Nobody knew her. There must be another Anna. She glanced around quickly. There were no other girls in sight. Only a tall boy coming along the sidewalk from the opposite direction.

Anna dropped her gaze hastily and quickened her steps. She was almost sure he had been looking right at her and smiling but her new glasses must be playing tricks. She did not know that boy.

They met where the walk led into the school building.

"What's the matter? You deaf?" the boy asked.

He was laughing a little.

Anna darted another glance up at him and then stared at her shoes again.

It's Bernard, she thought, feeling sick.

She was not positive, but she had better answer. Bernard was Rudi's size exactly.

"I am not deaf," she told him.

Her voice was thin and small.

"Good," the boy said. "Hey, why don't you look at me."

Obediently, Anna lifted her head. He was still laughing. Sometimes when Rudi teased, he laughed too.

"That's better," the boy said. "Now I'm going to do you a favor."

Anna had no idea what he was talking about. She was certain now, though, that he was Bernard. She longed to run but something firm in the way he spoke to her made her stay facing him, waiting.

"This will be your first lesson in being a good Canadian," he went on.

"Lesson?" Anna repeated like a parrot.

Her voice was a little stronger now.

"Yeah, lesson. When you hear somebody say, 'Hi, Anna,' the way I did, you say 'Hi' back again."

He paused. Anna stared at him.

"You say, 'Hi, Bernard!'" he prompted.

Anna just stood, still not understanding, still not quite brave enough to run.

"Come on or we're both going to be late," he urged. "Just say 'Hi, Bernard.' That's not so hard to say, is it?"

"Hi," Anna heard herself whisper.

She could not manage to add his name. What did "Hi" mean anyway? Bernard grinned.

"That's a start," he said. "See you in class, kid."

He loped up the walk, leaving her behind. Anna followed slowly.

Somehow she had done the right thing. Bernard had not been mean. But what had it all been about?

She was so puzzled that she was inside the school before she remembered how afraid she was.

Then the nightmare began. She could not find the right classroom. She wandered up one long hall, down another. Through open doorways, she caught sight of groups of children but she recognized nobody. Several boys and girls hurried past her. They all knew exactly where they were going. If one had stopped long enough, she might have been able to ask the way but nobody seemed to see her.

A bell clanged. Anna jumped. Then everywhere the doors were closed.

She went on walking past the tall shut doors. She tried not to think of Papa. She tried not to think at all. She just walked and walked and walked.

"Anna! Anna! This way!"

Footsteps clattered after her. Angel footsteps! But the angel was Isobel, her ringlets bouncing, her eyes warm with sympathy.

"Bernard said he'd seen you so we guessed you must be lost," she explained.

She grabbed Anna's cold hand and squeezed it.

"I know exactly how you feel," she told the new girl, tugging her along, not seeming to mind that Anna could not speak a word in return. "I got lost six times my first week here. This school is so big and all the halls look the same. At recess, I'll show you a sure way to remember. You just have to come in the right door, climb two sets of stairs, turn right and you're there. Here, I mean," she finished.

Before them, like a miracle, was the right door. It stood open. Nobody was working. Benjamin wasn't even in his desk. He was at the door watching for them. In an instant, Miss Williams was there too.

"Oh, Anna, I'm sorry I wasn't there to meet you," she said.

Anna let Isobel lead her to her desk. She sank into her seat. She listened. Apparently everyone in the class had been lost at least once in the school building. Nobody blamed Anna. Not once did anyone say, "How stupid of you not to have paid better attention yesterday!"

"I got lost once just coming back from the bathroom," Ben said and blushed.

The rest laughed. Ben didn't seem to mind. He smiled himself.

"I expect you were daydreaming, Ben," Miss Williams commented.

"I was figuring out whether a person could dig a tunnel under the Atlantic Ocean," Benjamin admitted.

The class laughed again. Anna stopped trembling. Here in Canada, she thought, maybe it is all right to make mistakes.

"Now it's time we stopped gossiping," Miss Williams told them. "Take your place, Ben."

Ben went to his desk. Miss Williams moved to stand at the front of the room. As she opened her mouth to begin, a voice spoke up.

"Hi, Anna," Bernard said.

Anna looked at him. Then she looked at the teacher. Miss Williams was smiling, waiting. Anna gripped the edge of her desk.

"Hi, Bernard," she said, still in a whisper.

"I'm teaching her to be a Canadian," Bernard explained.

Miss Williams did not look surprised.

"Good," she said simply. "Class, stand."

When it was time for recess, Isobel did not forget. Ben came along too. They took Anna to the door through which she would enter the school.

"It's the door you'd come to naturally, walking from your place," Isobel said.

Anna's surprise showed on her face. How did Isobel know where the Soldens lived?

"I heard Dr. Schumacher tell Miss Williams your address yesterday," Isobel confessed. "I live on the same street, two blocks this way. Now listen, you come in here..."

"Cross-eyed...cross-eyed!" a voice in the playground sang out.

Anna did not know what the words meant. Until she saw her stiffen, she did not know they had anything to do with Isobel.

"Ignore them, Isobel," Ben urged. "Pretend you don't even hear, like Miss Williams said."

"Four-eyes...four-eyes!" another voice took up the mocking chant.

Isobel let the school door close, shutting the three of them safely inside. She smiled shakily at Ben.

"Ignore them yourself, Benjamin," she advised.

"I hate them!" Ben said, through clenched teeth.

"Me too...but hating doesn't help," Isobel said. "It would if we were a lot bigger."

She caught the bewilderment on Anna's face. "She doesn't know what they mean," she said to Ben.

She explained about crossed eyes. Anna did not get all the words but she understood the gestures. Isobel's eyes did cross sometimes but they were nice eyes, brown and kind. Anna remembered the brightness in them that morning when Isobel had found her. She, like Ben, hated whoever called Isobel names.

"Four-eyes" meant glasses. Ben pointed to his eyes and then to each of his rounded lenses, counting them up.

"Four," he finished.

Anna looked at his earnest face. She hesitated. Could she make herself understood? Then she tried.

"Maybe I was it," she told him.

Ben looked at Isobel for help.

"What did you say?" Isobel asked Anna.

That hateful English! She should have known better than to attempt it. Then in a flash, Anna knew what to do. She imitated Ben, pointing to her own eyes and lenses as she counted.

"Ohhhh," Ben and Isobel said together. They laughed, the tension leaving their faces.

"Join the crowd," Isobel said.

As she spoke, she put her arm around Anna's shoulders and hugged her quickly, lightly.

"Come on. We're showing her how to find the room," Ben reminded them.

Anna followed her guides. She did not know what "join the crowd" meant exactly, but she was suddenly glad she had tried out her English.

Then, as she climbed the stairs with the other two, she remembered the tormenting singsong voices outside and she scowled. So there were boys like Rudi in Canada too. She had been wrong about Bernard, but there were others.

She had been very wrong about Bernard. He spoke to her again that afternoon when school was over and he was about to leave.

"So long, Anna," he said.

Anna did not know it but she reminded Bernard of a stray cat. He had rescued so many stray cats that his mother had refused to let him in the door with one ever again. Now he waited for Anna to answer him. He did not hurry her. You had to be gentle and patient with strays.

At last Anna responded.

"So long?" she said, making a question out of it.

"It just means 'Good-bye till later,'" the boy explained. She understood—it meant *"Auf wiedersehen."*

He smiled at her and left, forgetting her the moment she was out of sight.

Anna did not forget. All the way to Papa's store, she thought and thought about Bernard.

A bell chimed when she opened the door. Anna listened for it. It was as though the store said "Hi, Anna."

It is a Canadian store, she thought.

Papa was busy. Anna did not mind. She drifted back to a shadowy corner and perched on an upended orange crate. Already she had chosen this dim room, so crowded with things and yet so peaceful as a refuge. Even Papa did not have a lot of time to notice her here. Sometimes it was nice not being noticed. Sometimes you had things to think about, private things.

She could see Papa weighing some cheese for a plump lady. She watched him count oranges into a bag. But she was not thinking about him.

"Hi, Bernard," whispered Anna. "So long, Bernard."

Now Papa was climbing up a set of steps to get down a mousetrap.

I could say it to the others too maybe, Anna thought. Hi, Isobel. So long, Ben.

She gasped at her own daring. Yet one of these days, she might.

The stout lady said, "Thank you, Mr. Solden," and went out.

Isobel put her arm around me, remembered Anna.

Papa was the only person who hugged her. When anyone else tried, she went stiff and jerked away. She could not help it. Sometimes she did not even want to. But she still did.

"Anna's not a loving child," Mama had said once to Aunt Tania when Anna had squirmed away from a kiss.

But today, with Isobel, it had been different.

No fuss, thought Anna. Just nice.

Papa had turned. He was peering through the shadows, looking for her. Anna waited for him to find her in her corner. They smiled at each other across the store.

"Good afternoon, Anna," her father said.

She looked at him. In all her world, he was the kindest person. He would not laugh at her even if she got it wrong. Papa never laughed at her when he knew she was serious. She took a deep breath.

"Hi, Papa," said Anna in a loud, brave voice. It sounded fine.

Where Could We Escape To?

♦ ♦ ♦

BY

HARRY

PINIUTA

e had arrived at Kapuskasing, the site of special camps for aliens. Here we were assigned to the different barracks. Mine was barrack number three. As soon as I went in, I was surrounded by a number of inmates. They were, for the most part, Ukrainians from Galicia. They bombarded me with questions: "Where did you come from? Where were you captured? How is the war progressing? Is it true that the Russians were driven out of Galicia?" and so on.

Towards evening, the barrack swarmed with men returning from their work. Then came the call for supper. The meal consisted of a spoonful of sauerkraut and a potato served on a tin plate, and tea served in a tin cup. There was plenty of bread and half a gallon of jam to go with it. We newcomers, famished while awaiting supper, cleaned up every last morsel of our food. After supper, the barrack hummed with conversation until nine o'clock. Then came the curfew, and everybody was off to bed.

The snow continued to fall without a letup. In a few days, it was knee-deep. Every day, it got deeper and deeper. The temperature dropped to thirty and forty degrees below zero. Notwithstanding the deep snow and the bitter cold, the men, guarded by soldiers armed with rifles, continued to cut brush in the woods.

In all, there were over 1300 men in the camp. The majority of them were young men, between twenty and thirty years of age; the rest were from thirty to fifty years old. One-third of them were Ukrainians from Galicia, and the others were Croats, Poles, and Hungarians. There were also a few hundred Turks, but they were lodged in separate barracks.

Finally Easter Sunday came, gray and dull. And it went by like any other Sunday with one significant exception—there was no work for us that day. To hold a service of worship was out of the question as there was no priest. The men sat the day out in the barracks, silent, depressed, and wrapped up in their somber thoughts. Only now and then someone would softly strike up *"Khrystos Voskres."* Each one was weighed down by his own misery. The thought that gnawed most fiercely at all of us was "How long is our punishment going to go on? When are we going to be out of here, free once again?"

One day, barrack number four was ordered to vacate. Its inmates were assigned to other barracks. We were told that number four was to get 100 new occupants.

And, indeed, one afternoon a couple of days later, a train arrived with a transport of new internees. As soon as they got off, they were taken by guards to the vacant barrack number four.

We were appalled by the appearance of these men. Their faces were yellowed and emaciated, and they all looked haggard —old and young, without exception. It was a frightful sight. We tried to find out from them where they had been rounded up. Their speech was hard to understand, for they all spoke with difficulty—some through tears. They complained that they had not yet had a morsel of food in their mouths that day.

We got busy and collected several coupons to buy food for them. Each one of us donated as many as he could, and we exchanged them for a couple of oranges and a chocolate bar for each of the new arrivals. That was all that was available in the canteen.

For supper, they were served the same kind of meal as we were, but some of them had lost their appetites completely and did not eat at all.

After supper, we listened to their stories about their hard lot. They had been interned in the camp near Petawawa. There were 600 of them in all. All were forced to do hard labour. When the Feast of Annunciation rolled around, the internees at the camp asked for a day off from work to observe the holy day. But it was not to be. No one paid any attention to their request. The commander of the camp responded with "To hell with your holy day," and the internees were all ordered to go to work that day.

The next day, no one turned up for work. All of them, to the last man, stayed in the barracks. The camp officials summoned them one by one to the office and demanded an explanation of why they refused to go to work. The one most important question, which was asked of each internee, was "Why don't you want to work?"

They all had a ready answer. One replied, "You did not capture me on the battlefield. I came to Canada not to fight a war but to earn a living and to enrich this country with my labours." Another argued, "I am already forty years old. I always observed that holy day in the same way as did my grandparents and my great-grandparents. My ancestors shed their blood for the privilege of observing this and other holy days, and here you are forcing me to commit sacrilege by going to work on a holy day. I would rather be put to death on this day than trample upon my faith."

A third one had this explanation: "Before I came to this country I heard that there was freedom of religion and speech here, that everyone had the right to abstain from work on his holy day. But you would not let us observe our holy day, and you mock us, besides. Not one of us whom you have locked up here is responsible for the war in any way. But you have desecrated a holy day, and for that you will answer before God."

In the end, one of them declared in the name of the entire group, "Because you are forcing us to work on a holy day, we are not going back to work ever."

At eight o'clock in the evening, an officer visited barrack number four and gave the newcomers a short talk. He told them that other men at the barracks had worked faithfully over the past two years and obediently discharged their duties. They received good meals, clothes, and pay, and they were satisfied. When he finished praising the former inmates of the barrack, he reminded the men that there was a war on and one must obey wartime regulations passed by the government. Then he asked, "Will you go to work tomorrow?"

From all around came the resounding answer, "No! No! No!"

We were perturbed by their story. We asked our new comrades in captivity whether it was worth their while to lay themselves open to further persecution.

They replied, "Calm yourselves; we are not afraid of persecution." And they recounted the instances of persecution they had experienced every time that they refused to work. "Our food rations were immediately reduced by one-half, the straw from our bunks was removed, and our warm clothing was taken away from us. We were forced to run, fall to the ground, and rise to our feet again repeatedly while we were being flogged. We were forced to carry fifty-pound bags of sand a distance of thirty miles. Our daily food ration continued to be progressively reduced until we had only bread and water. One hundred of us were transferred to this camp. What is going to happen to the ones left behind we do not know, but we are not going to work here either."

Deep down within us, we admired their decision and their determination to stand up for their rights. Their spirit was praiseworthy. They put us to shame for our submissiveness and slavish acquiescence to servility. In our hearts, a new spark of indignation was kindled, but we remained silent.

The next day, the guard unbolted the door of barrack number four and ordered the men to work. Not a soul stirred. In the brief moment of silence which ensued, one could have heard a pin drop.

Around ten o'clock, all the occupants of barrack number four were chased out and summoned one by one to the major's office. Each one individually was asked why he did not want to go to work. Some pleaded sickness. They were sent back to the barrack. Others replied that since they were not captured on the battlefront, they did not consider themselves prisoners of war, and no one had the right to force them to work.

Out of 100 men, only the 9 who pleaded illness were allowed to return to the barrack. The rest of them were punched and pushed and shoved forcibly out of the office by the soldiers. They were assembled in one spot where they were arranged in files of four. Soon, more soldiers arrived from the barracks and surrounded the captives on all sides. The major, the captain, and the lieutenant emerged from the office and ordered the men to proceed towards the barrack.

The unique parade moved slowly forward as some 300 of us looked on. As the procession approached us, a young voice suddenly called out from among the spectators, "Hey, fellows, these men are being marched to their torture. They are our brothers; let's protect them!"

In fact, that was exactly how every single one of us felt, but none had dared to make the first move. Now that call, like a marching order, prompted an immediate response from us. We all rushed to block the advance of the procession. It ground to a halt. One Polish fellow from our group strode up to within a step of the major. The major pulled out his revolver and fired a shot into the air. He then used it to hit the Pole on his bald head and knock him to the ground.

The men raised an uproar,

yelling, shouting, and whistling. In the midst of the clamour, one could hear their calls of "Shame! Beat him up! Stone him!"

There was confusion among the troops. The major gave the signal to sound the trumpet, and the soldiers rushed at us with fixed bayonets. We scurried away and headed for the barracks.

Those with minor wounds treated themselves in the barracks. Nine men were seriously wounded and had to be hospitalized.

This incident was a turning point for us. We all resolved to ignore every order to go to work. Our food rations were reduced by half, but we did not worry about that. Persuasion did not move us, and threats did not scare us.

A few days later, a special commission arrived to investigate the incident.

News of the incident spread far and wide. News items and editorials appeared in Canadian and American newspapers, with reverberations in all parts of the world.

Shortly after the investigation, we were all set free. This convinced us that freedom can be won if we are ready to shed blood for it. We should never take freedom for granted.

At first no one wanted to leave the camp. Some said they would not move from the place until they were paid for two years of their lost time. Others demanded assurance that they would be returned to the jobs from which they were torn away.

The administration of the camp was helpless; for a long time, the inmates refused to abandon the camp. Eventually, however, the camp began to break up, and the inmates left one by one, each going his own way. Memories of the camp gradually began to fade away. But one could never really forget it completely.

A Child
in Prison Camp

♦ ♦ ♦

BY SHIZUYE TAKASHIMA

In December 1941, 22 000 men, women, and children of Japanese origin were living on Canada's West Coast.

Within a few months every one of them — whether Canadian-born, naturalized citizen, or new immigrant — was stripped of all civil rights and submitted to three years of indignity on a scale that makes the episode the most disgraceful in the country's history.

The story of that time as it was experienced by one family, and particularly one young girl, is here told by Canadian artist Takashima. She tells it gently, without hatred or anger, as if she would protect us from its full harshness just as her parents tried to protect her. It somehow makes the courage the more terrible.

And unjustifiable by all civilized standards — since no Japanese-Canadian ever committed, or was even accused of, a single act of espionage or sabotage. Yet their farms, homes, stores, and fishing vessels were confiscated. Older sons were sent to internment camps in the Rocky Mountains to build primitive shacks that would house their families for the next three years.

Vancouver, British Columbia
March 1942

Japan is at war with the United States, Great Britain and all the Allied Countries, including Canada, the country of my birth. My parents are Japanese, born in Japan, but they have been Canadian citizens for many, many years, and have become part of this young country. Now, overnight our rights as Canadians are taken away. Mass evacuation for the Japanese!

"All the Japanese," it is carefully explained to me, "whether we were born in Tokyo or in Vancouver are to be moved to distant places. Away from the west coast of British Columbia—for security reasons."

We must all leave, my sister, Yuki, my older brother David, my parents, our relatives—all.

The older men are the first to go. The government feels that my father, or his friends, might sabotage the police and their buildings. Imagine! I couldn't believe such stories, but there is my father packing just his clothes in a small suitcase.

Yuki says, "They are going to the foothills of the Rockies, at Tête Jaune. No one's there, and I guess they feel father won't bomb the mountains."

The older people are very frightened. Mother is so upset; so are all her friends. I, being only eleven, seem to be on the outside.

One March day, we go to the station to see father board the train.

At the Train Station

An empty bottle is tossed in the air. I stand away, hold my mother's hand. Angry, dark curses, a scream. A train window is broken.

Most of the men have been drinking. An angry man is shouting. The men are dragged violently into the trains. Father can be seen. He is being pushed onto the train. He is on the steps, turns. His head is above the shouting crowd. I see his mouth opening; he shouts to his friends, waves his clenched fist. But the words are lost in all the noise. Mother holds my hand tightly.

A sharp police whistle blows. My blood stops. We see a uniformed Mounted Police drag an old man and hurl him into the train. More curses, threats. The old train bellows its starting sound. White, hellish smoke appears from the top of its head. It grunts, gives another shrill blast. Slowly, slowly, the engine comes to life. I watch from where we stand, fascinated. The huge, black, round, ugly wheels begin to move slowly, then faster and faster. Finally, the engine, jet dark, rears its body and moves with a lurch. The remaining men rush toward the train, scramble quickly into the moving machine.

Men crowd at the windows. Father is still on the steps, he seems to be searching the crowd, finally sees us, waves. Mother does not move. Yuki and I wave. Most remain still. The dark, brown faces of the men become small. Some are still shouting. Yuki moves closer to mother.

The long, narrow, old train quickly picks up speed as it coils away along the tracks away from all of us who are left at the station.

Mother is silent. I look at her. I see tears are slowly falling. They remain on her cheeks. I turn away, look around. The women and the children stare at one another. Some women cry right out loud. A bent old woman breaks out into a Buddhist prayer, moves her orange beads in her wrinkled hands, prays aloud to her God. Mother and the other women bow their heads. The silent god seems so far away.

Spring 1944

The war with Japan is getting very bad. I can feel my parents growing anxious. There is a lot of tension in the camp; rumors of being moved again, of everyone having to return to Japan. Kazuo and his family leave for Japan. Many are angry they have left us. Some call them cowards, others call them brave! I only feel sad, for I liked Kazuo so much, so very much.

Father shouts at Mother, "We return to Japan!" "But what are we going to do? You have your brothers and sisters there. I have no one. Besides, the children…" "Never mind the children," father answers. "They'll adjust. I'm tired of being treated as a spy, a prisoner. Do what you like; I'm returning!"

I can see Mrs. Kono looks confused. "My husband is talking of returning to Japan, too. I think it's the best thing. All our relatives are still there. We have nothing here." Yuki stares at her. "It's all right for you, Mrs. Kono, you were born there, but we weren't. I'm not going. That's all!" And she walks out of the house.

Mother gets very upset. I know she wants to cry. "I don't want to go to Japan, either," I say. "They're short of food and clothing there. They haven't enough for their own people. They won't want us back."

All of a sudden I hate that country for having started the war. I say aloud, "Damn Japs! Why don't they stop fighting?" Father glares. "What do you mean 'Japs'? You think you're not a Jap? If I hear you say that again I'll throttle you." I see anger and hatred in his eyes. I leave the room, go out of the house. I hear him say loudly to Mother, "It's all your fault. You poison our children's minds by saying we're better off here."

And another argument starts. I am getting tired of it, and confused. I feel so helpless, and wish again I were older, then maybe I could go somewhere…But I do not hate the people in Japan. I know Yuki doesn't hate them either, really. It's all so senseless. Really, maybe children should rule the world! Yuki tells me it is wrong for Father, because of his anger at the wrong done towards him and us, to expect us to return to his country: "Sure, we're Japanese. But we think like Canadians. We won't be accepted in Japan if we go there."

August 1945
We hear the terrifying news. The atomic bomb! Father and Mother are silent. Mrs. Kono looks so upset. I go to see Mary. Her mother is crying. There is a terrible tension in the camp. Mr. Mori and the other veterans are openly cursed and threatened. Some blame them for the bomb. No one speaks to Mr. Mori. I saw him this morning. He stared at me. He held his stick very tight to his thin body. I backed away and turned, for I didn't want to pass him. I wondered what he thought as I hurried into the house. I can't understand all this hatred, especially among ourselves....

The End of the War
At last the war with Japan is at an end! We are not surprised, we have been expecting it for months now. It hits the older people very hard. They are given two choices by the Canadian Government: to sign a paper and renounce their Canadian citizenship and return to Japan, or to remain here and be relocated elsewhere. There are terrible quarrels. Those who have signed to return to Japan are called "fools"; the ones who have chosen to stay in Canada are called "dogs," slang for traitors. The Kono family, Mr. Shimizu, our father's friend, all sign to return to Japan. We feel sad that Kay-ko is leaving us. All those families must move to another camp, at Tashme, not far from Vancouver. From there, they will go to Vancouver, then on to Japan.

My mother and I just wait, hoping. Then one day, out of the blue, Father says quietly: "We go east! I've placed an application. We sign to go to Toronto." He speaks quietly, more to Mother than to me. "It is useless to return now. My family, God knows where they are, if any are still alive. I'm glad it's over. We'll just have to start again. It won't be easy for us." He looks strange. He rises from his chair quickly and walks out. I feel sorry for him. The atomic bomb has upset everyone deeply, too. It seems so wrong. Mother looks at me, smiles. Her eyes beam. "See, I told you, I told you, he would see the sense in remaining here. We can't return to Japan. They have nothing now, no food, no clothes, houses for their own people. Here, we have each other. Write to Yuki and David." I write immediately.

Yuki is in Hamilton, Ontario, living with another friend. I am so happy, so is Mother. Father is quiet, but he starts to make boxes with our cousin, Mr. Fujiwara, the carpenter, to pack our clothes in. Our cousins are remaining in camps a while longer, but they, too, have signed to stay in Canada.

Mother and I begin to pack. I have to leave many things I have grown to love behind. My favorite "dutch shoe" which Yuki gave me almost two Christmases ago is still by my bed, on the narrow shelf near the candle. I pick it up. The candies and nuts are gone. The sparkly, gold rice is dull, many grains have already fallen off; more drop into my hand. But as I hold it I can still feel the love which the kind Sisters put into it just when we needed love so much. I place it back on the shelf. It is too fragile to pack.

September 1945

It is almost three years to the day since we left Vancouver. The papers for us to leave for the east come through. This is our last week in New Denver.

I go to the lake for the last time with Mother to rinse our clothes. The water is still warm. I swish the white sheets in the clear water. Mother is wringing the clothes. She is singing, she looks so happy. I wonder what David will look like. I say, "We won't be doing this in Toronto." Mother sighs, stops, looks at the mountains. "All in all, Shichan, the three years have not been very hard, when you think of all the poor people who have been killed and hurt, and now the suffering in Japan."

Mother and I look out into the distance. A small bird swoops gracefully down towards the still water. Another follows. Their pure joy in doing this is reflected in their flight. The morning mist is slowly rising from the lake. It looks like it is on fire. The sun's rays try to seep through the mist. Everything looks all misty and gray-yellow. I know I shall remember this beautiful scene, doing our chores for the last time with nature all-giving and so silent. Mother bends her frail body, continues to rinse the clothes. I go back to helping her. There is warmth between us, and I feel her happiness.

I try to absorb it all, for I know it will be gone soon. Toronto is a large city. David has written it is in flat country, by Lake Ontario. There are no mountains, no snow-capped mountains. Instead will be concrete buildings, apartments, buses, cars. But I am looking forward to this, too. Instead of the sounds of insects and frogs and wild dogs at night, we will have street sounds, and go to school with other children, all kinds of children.

Our last night in camp, I go out of the house. I watch the red rays of the glorious sun. It spreads its burning arms to the brilliant early autumn sky, touches the dark pines in the distance. They catch fire. I hold my breath. It is aflame, all red for a long time.

Then the rays of the sun slowly begin to fade behind the now deep purple mountains. The trees, the mountains all turn into a dark mysterious silhouette as I stay rooted to the spot. Night comes on. The pale, pale moon is suspended in the scarlet sky. I stay standing a long time watching it, for I want to remember it forever.

Epilogue
Toronto, Ontario
June 7, 1964

Nineteen years have passed. Tonight I have come here to watch the end of a story. I am standing before a gray concrete, fortresslike building with a crowd of my people, all Japanese-Canadians. They have come from all over Ontario to be at this outdoor ceremony. After years of planning and money-raising, the Japanese Canadian Cultural Centre is ready.

It is early evening. The late spring sun casts a warm ochre glow over everything. I stand towards the back of the crowd. The older people are seated at the front, but Father and Mother are not there. "I don't want to go," Father said earlier when I asked him. The years have lined his face and tinged his spiky black hair with gray, but they have not softened his intensity. I looked at Mother. Her gold-rimmed glasses flashed. "I'll stay home with your father tonight."

But many others are here. Yuki, with her husband and three children. Patty, the youngest, comes to stand beside me, takes my hand. "Mommy's wearing a new hat." I laugh, we all laugh and Yuki makes a face at Patty. Yuki is still very close to me. After all these years our love for each other has not changed. I see David in the distance with his wife and four children. They look like tiny theater dolls, with their dark hair, snappy round eyes, all dressed up. Patty calls to them. They wave back and jump up and down. Further on, I see the Kono family. After moving to Tashme on the coast, at the last minute—like many other families—they changed their minds and asked permission to remain in Canada. They had difficult years working in northern Ontario and had finally moved to Toronto. They are still our friends. Kay-ko is married now, but her round, beautiful eyes are still the same. I continue to search the crowd. Our cousins, the Fujiwaras, are away down front with the older people.

Suddenly, a hush falls over the crowd. A shiny black limousine pulls up. Everyone turns, watching it. A group of officials has been waiting for it. They move forward as the door is opened. Out of it gets a smiling man and woman: the Prime Minister of Canada, Lester B. Pearson, and Mrs. Pearson. We watch them go towards the platform.

As the speeches start, my mind wanders back, tracing the years.

We moved east from the camp, only to find that the quota of Japanese permitted to live in Toronto is filled, and there are no jobs. My parents go to work as domestic servants for an American family in Oakville, Father to do the gardening and cooking and mother to clean and care for their small child. I cannot join them, Father tells me gently, for the estate is in the country and there are no schools nearby. He talks it over with Mother and David, and I am to go to Hamilton to stay with Yuki. David will send the money for me to continue school.

The Oakville family is very kind—not all of our friends are so lucky—and we are allowed to come and see our parents. At Christmas, the family leaves for a holiday in Mexico and all of us, Yuki, David and I, come for the holidays. Mother looks so happy and Father cooks and outdoes himself. We seem to feast and rejoice for days.

At high school in Hamilton I take art as my major subject. The next summer, I get a job as summer help to a family with three children. I like the children but not their mother who makes what were to be "light duties" very heavy, and had somewhere got the idea that Japanese don't like to eat. In the fall of 1946, David helps us to buy a house in Toronto and we can all be together again. Father finds work in Toronto as a gardener and part-time cook for another wealthy family. They are so kind and generous that father stays there until he retires fourteen years later.

I finish high school, go on to the Ontario College of Art. At graduation, Father and Mother make me a gift from the savings they have gathered so slowly through the years so that I can go to Europe to continue my studies. Yuki marries, David marries, and a new generation starts, unclouded by those things that happened to their parents so long ago….

I focus back on the voices from the platform. The Prime Minister is introduced. He talks of all the fine things Japanese-Canadians have done for Canada; I feel a nervous tension go through the crowd as he comes to the hardships we suffered during World War II:

" …The action of the Canadian Government of the day—though taken under the strains and fears and pressures and irrationalities of war—was a black mark against Canada's traditional fairness and devotion to the principles of human rights. We have no reason to be proud of this episode nor are we… "

I look at the faces near me and feel the private silence of each listener. Some stare at their laps; others have their eyes closed. Some stare out at the sky, eyes moist. I look up too, and see the vast orange sky…I remember how often I stood outside our house in the New Denver camp and watched the sun set. The sun, the sky look the same, still beautiful, patient, so knowing…

Afterwards I go back to my parents' house. Mother brings green tea. Mother sits beside Father. They are inseparable now. Mother looks at me and smiles. Her small face is imprinted with the hardship of the years, her silvery hair is grown thin, but her eyes behind her round glasses are the same, warm.

Mother and I sip tea. The room is still. I say, "The Prime Minister said that what Canada did was wrong. Did you hear?" Father replies stiffly, "Yes, I heard it on the radio." Mother and I look at him and wait. He takes a drink from his glass, puts it down, stares at it. Then with gusto he takes another, longer drink that drains the glass. At last he speaks, looking straight ahead of him. "I'm glad the Prime Minister said that."

Mother nods and nudges him. They both look at me. I feel their happiness come toward me, and I smile back.

Acknowledgement

s a people, Canadians commit themselves to the creation of a society that ensures equality and justice for all, regardless of race or ethnic origin.

During and after World War II, Canadians of Japanese ancestry, the majority of whom were citizens, suffered unprecedented actions taken by the Government of Canada against their community.

Despite perceived military necessities at the time, the forced removal and internment of Japanese Canadians during World War II and their deportation and expulsion following the war, was unjust. In retrospect, government policies of disenfranchisement, detention, confiscation and sale of private and community property, expulsion, deportation and restriction of movement, which continued after the war, were influenced by discriminatory attitudes. Japanese Canadians who were interned had their property liquidated and the proceeds of sale were used to pay for their own internment.

The acknowledgement of these injustices serves notice to all Canadians that the excesses of the past are condemned and that the principles of justice and equality in Canada are reaffirmed.

Therefore, the Government of Canada, on behalf of all Canadians, does hereby:

1) acknowledge that the treatment of Japanese Canadians during and after World War II was unjust and violated principles of human rights as they are understood today;

2) pledge to ensure, to the full extent that its powers allow, that such events will not happen again; and

3) recognize, with great respect, the fortitude and determination of Japanese Canadians who, despite great stress and hardship, retain their commitment and loyalty to Canada and contribute so richly to the development of the Canadian nation.

Kanadalainen

♦ ♦ ♦

BY

NANCY

MATTSON

To have left behind the language
that flowed like spring water
the easy seepage
of fresh words every hour

To have come to a land
of thorough drought
with a dry tongue

To have to pump the handle
like a child again
lifted off the platform
by every upstroke
the pump so stiff
the well so dark
you doubt the alkali earth
will ever release its sour water

To hang a new pail
from the knuckle
on the pump mouth
watching the water trickle
slowly at first
    then slowly faster
    until the pail is overflowing
only to stumble on a root
on the path to the house

To watch the pumped water
settle and seep
into insatiable
Canadian earth

To have believed the words
would ever flow together
into sentences

Immigrants: The Second Generation

♦ ♦ ♦

BY KEVIN IRIE

The streets are
always crowded on
weekends, wide enough
to hold the world —
Asians, Indians,
Europeans as well.

One boy grows
from his mother's grip —
held that tightly.
Together they travel
in search of cheap pants,

the mother cursing
the high price of denim,
leaving it to the boy
to translate her ire
into English tact
for the smiling salesman
who politely informs them that, no,
there is nothing else.

English is standard currency here;

the boy knows that,
he hoards his small allotment
of words like
a miser his pennies,
the one allowance no one can confiscate.

Out here, he is
the word and the way; his first
language fell away like milk teeth.
Only his mother,
stranded by his side,
still speaks in the old tongue alone.

A few English phrases
glint in her mouth
like fillings placed there
by other hands: a foreign substance
given for her own good:
hard, and impacted for life.

I Want My Chaos Back

(August 28, 1983: Harbourfront, Toronto)

◆ ◆ ◆

BY

SURJEET

KALSEY

Today I am three thousand miles away
from throbbing bubbling figurines of
my flesh...how much I miss their presence...
how much...the very thought of not being
with them makes my heart droop.
The honest voices,
                    the soft touches
the house filled with their noise
I am dying to hear, to feel.
This is a real loneliness.
This is a real barrenness.

I want to walk with you all.
            I want my chaos back.
I miss the noise.
I miss the confusing sounds of my two
passions: children and creativity.
What I have created in the company of
you my love, I would never be able to
create without you. I miss you all
very much. Your presence, our noise,
I want my chaos back.
Touch me on this piece of paper,
        sending you in it lots of love.

Why My Mother Can't Speak English

◆ ◆ ◆

BY

GARRY ENGKENT

My mother is seventy years old. Widowed for five years now, she lives alone in her own house except for the occasions when I come home to tidy her household affairs. She has been in *gum san,* the golden mountain, for the past thirty years. She clings to the old-country ways so much so that today she astonishes me with this announcement:

"I want to get my citizenship," she says as she slaps down the *Dai Pao,* "before they come and take away my house."

"Nobody's going to do that. This is Canada."

"So everyone says," she retorts, "but did you read what the *Dai Pao* said? Ah, you can't read Chinese. The government is cutting back on old-age pensions. Anybody who hasn't got citizenship will lose everything. Or worse."

"The *Dai Pao* can't even typeset accurately," I tell her. Sometimes I worry about the information Mother receives from that biweekly community newspaper. "Don't worry—the Ministry of Immigration won't send you back to China."

"Little you know," she snaps back. "I am old, helpless, and without citizenship. Reasons enough. Now, get me citizenship. Hurry!"

"Mother, getting citizenship papers is not like going to the bank to cash in your pension cheque. First, you have to—"

"Excuses, my son, excuses. When your father was alive—"

"Oh, Mother, not again! You throw that at me every—"

"—made excuses, too." Her jaw tightens. "If you can't do this little thing for your own mother, well, I will just have to go and beg your cousin to…"

Every time I try to explain about the ways of the *fan gwei,* she thinks I do not want to help her.

"I'll do it, I'll do it, okay? Just give me some time."

"That's easy for you," Mother snorts. "You're not seventy years old. You're not going to lose your pension. You're not going to lose your house. Now, how much *lai-shi* will this take?"

After all these years in *gum san* she cannot understand that you don't give government officials *lai-shi,* the traditional Chinese money gift to persons who do things for you.

"That won't be necessary," I tell her. "And you needn't go to my cousin."

Mother picks up the *Dai Pao* again and says: "Why should I beg at the door of a village cousin when I have a son who is a university graduate?"

I wish my father were alive. Then he would be doing this. But he is not here, and as a dutiful son, I am responsible for the welfare of my widowed mother. So I take her to Citizenship Court.

There are several people from the Chinese community waiting there. Mother knows a few of the Chinese women and she chats with them. My cousin is there, too.

"I thought your mother already got her citizenship," he says to me. "Didn't your father—"

"No, he didn't."

He shakes his head sadly. "Still, better now than never. That's why I'm getting these people through."

"So they've been reading the *Dai Pao.*"

He gives me a quizzical look, so I explain to him, and he laughs.

"You are the new generation," he says. "You didn't live long enough in *hon san,* the sweet land, to understand the fears of the old. You can't expect the elderly to renounce all attachments to China for the ways of the *fan gwei.* How old is she, seventy now? Much harder."

"She woke me up this morning at six, and Citizenship Court doesn't open until ten."

The doors of the court finally open, and Mother motions me to hurry. We wait in line for a while.

The clerk distributes applications and tells me the requirements. Mother wants to know what the clerk is saying, so half the time I translate for her.

The clerk suggests that we see one of the liaison officers.

"Your mother has been living in Canada for the past thirty years and she still can't speak English?"

"It happens," I tell the liaison officer.

"I find it hard to believe that —not one word?"

"Well, she understands some restaurant English," I tell her. "You know, French fries, pork chops, soup, and so on. And she can say a few words."

"But will she be able to understand the judge's questions? The interview with the judge, as you know, is an important part of the citizenship procedure. Can she read the booklet? What does she know about Canada?"

"So you don't think my mother has a chance?"

"The requirements are that the candidate must be able to speak either French or English, the two official languages of Canada. The candidate must be able to pass an oral interview with the citizenship judge, and then he or she must be able to recite the oath of allegiance—"

"My mother needs to speak English," I conclude for her.

"Look, I don't mean to be rude, but why didn't your mother learn English when she first came over?"

I have not been translating this conversation, and Mother, annoyed and agitated, asks me what is going on. I tell her there is a slight problem.

"What problem?" Mother opens her purse, and I see her taking a small red envelope— *lai-shi*—I quickly cover her hand.

"What's going on?" the liaison officer demands.

"Nothing," I say hurriedly. "Just a cultural misunderstanding, I assure you."

My mother rattles off some indignant words, and I snap back in Chinese: "Put that away! The woman won't understand, and we'll be in a lot of trouble."

The officer looks confused, and I realize that an explanation is needed.

"My mother was about to give you a money gift as a token of appreciation for what you are doing for us. I was afraid you might misconstrue it as a bribe. We have no intention of doing that."

"I'm relieved to hear it."

We conclude the interview, and I take Mother home. Still clutching the application, Mother scowls at me.

"I didn't get my citizenship papers. Now I will lose my old-age pension. The government will ship me back to China. My old bones will lie there while your father's will be here. What will happen to me?"

How can I teach her to speak the language when she is too old to learn, too old to want to learn? She resists anything that is *fan gwei*. She does everything the Chinese way. Mother spends much time staring blankly at the four walls of her house. She does not cry. She sighs and shakes her head. Sometimes she goes about the house touching her favourite things.

"This is all your dead father's fault," she says quietly. She turns to the photograph of my father on the mantel. Daily, she burns incense, pours fresh cups of fragrant tea, and spreads dishes of his favourite fruits in front of the framed picture as is the custom. In memory of his passing, she treks two miles to the cemetery to place flowers by his headstone, to burn ceremonial paper money, and to talk to him. Regularly, rain or shine, or even snow, she does these things. Such love, such devotion, now such vehemence. Mother curses my father, her husband, in his grave.

When my mother and I emigrated from China, she was forty years old, and I, five. My father was already a well-established restaurant owner. He put me in school and Mother in the restaurant kitchen, washing dishes and cooking strange foods like hot dogs, hamburgers, and French fries. She worked seven days a week from six in the morning until eleven at night. This lasted for twenty-five years, almost to the day of my father's death.

The years were hard on her. The black-and-white photographs show a robust woman; now I see a withered, frail, white-haired old woman, angry, frustrated with the years, and scared of losing what little material wealth she has to show for the toil in *gum san*.

"I begged him," Mother says. "But he would either ignore my pleas or say: 'What do you need to know English for? You're better off here in the kitchen. Here you can talk to the others in our own tongue. English is far too complicated for you. How old are you now? Too old to learn a new language. Let the young speak *fan gwei*. All you need is to understand the orders from the waitresses. Anyway, if you need to know something, the men will translate for you. I am here; I can do your talking for you.'"

As a conscientious boss of the young male immigrants, my father would force them out of the kitchen and into the dining room. "The kitchen is no place for you to learn English. All you do is speak Chinese in here. To survive in *gum san,* you have to speak English, and the only way you can do that is to wait on tables and force yourselves to speak English with the customers. How can you get your families over here if you can't talk to the immigration officers in English?"

A few of the husbands who had the good fortune to bring their wives over to Canada hired a retired school teacher to teach a bit of English to their wives. Father discouraged Mother from going to those once-a-week sessions.

"That old woman will get rich doing nothing. What have these women learned? *Fan gwei* ways— make-up, lipstick, smelly perfumes, fancy clothes. Once she gets through with them, they won't be Chinese women any more—and they certainly won't be white either."

Some of the husbands heeded the words of the boss, for he was older than they, and he had been in the *fan gwei's* land longer. These wives stayed home and tended the children, or they worked in the restaurant kitchen, washing dishes and cooking *fan gwei* foods, and talking in Chinese about the land and the life they had been forced to leave behind.

"He was afraid that I would leave him. I depended on him for everything. I could not go anywhere by myself. He drove me to work and he drove me home. He only taught me how to print my name so that I could sign anything he wanted me to, bank cheques, legal documents…"

Perhaps I am not Chinese enough any more to understand why my mother would want to take in the sorrow, the pain, and the anguish, and then to recount them every so often.

Once, I was presumptuous enough to ask her why she would want to remember in such detail. She said that the memories didn't hurt any more. I did not tell her that her reminiscences cut me to the quick. Her only solace now is to be listened to.

When my father died five years ago, she cried and cried. "Don't leave me in this world. Let me die with you."

Grief-stricken, she would not eat for days. She was so weak from hunger that I feared she wouldn't be able to attend the funeral. At his grave side, she chanted over and over a dirge, commending his spirit to the next world and begging the goddess of mercy to be kind to him. By custom, she set his picture on the mantel and burned incense in front of it daily. And we would go to the cemetery often. There she would arrange fresh flowers and talk to him in the gentlest way.

Often she would warn me: "The world of the golden mountain is so strong, *fan gwei* improprieties, and customs. They will have you abandon your own aged mother to some old-age home to rot away and die unmourned. If you are here long enough, they will turn your head until you don't know who you are —Chinese."

My mother would convert the months and the days into the Chinese lunar calendar. She would tell me about the seasons and the harvests and festivals in China. We did not celebrate any *fan gwei* holidays.

My mother sits here at the table, fingering the booklet from the Citizenship Court. For thirty-some years, my mother did not learn the English language, not because she was not smart enough, not because she was too old to learn, and not because my father forbade her, but because she feared that learning English would change her Chinese soul. She only learned enough English to survive in the restaurant kitchen.

Now, Mother wants *gum san* citizenship.

"Is there no hope that I will be given it?" she asks.

"There's always a chance," I tell her. "I'll hand in the application."

"I should have given that person the *lai-shi,*" Mother says obstinately.

"Maybe I should teach you some English," I retort. "You have about six months before the oral interview."

"I am seventy years old," she says. *"Lai-shi* is definitely much easier."

My brief glimpse into Mother's heart is over, and it has taken so long to come about. I do not know whether I understand my aged mother any better now. Despite my mother's constant instruction, there is too much *fan gwei* in me.

The booklet from the Citizenship Court lies, unmoved, on the table, gathering dust for weeks. She has not mentioned citizenship again with the urgency of that particular time. Once in a while, she would say: "They have forgotten me. I told you they don't want old Chinese women as citizens."

Finally, her interview date is set. I try to teach her some ready-made phrases, but she forgets them.

"You should not sigh so much. It is bad for your health," Mother observes.

On the day of her examination, I accompany her into the judge's chamber. I am more nervous than my mother.

Staring at the judge, my mother remarks: *"Noi yren."* The judge shows interest in what my mother says, and I translate it: "She says you're a woman."

The judge smiles. "Yes. Is that strange?"

"If she is going to examine me," Mother tells me, "I might as well start packing for China. Sell my house. Dig up your father's bones, and I'll take them back with me."

Without knowing what my mother said, the judge reassures her. "This is just a formality. Really. We know that you obviously want to be part of our Canadian society. Why else would you go through all this trouble? We want to welcome you as a new citizen, no matter what race, nationality, religion, or age. And we want you to be proud— as a new Canadian."

Six weeks have passed since the interview with the judge. Mother receives a registered letter telling her to come in three weeks' time to take part in the oath of allegiance ceremony.

With patient help from the same judge, my mother recites the oath and becomes a Canadian citizen after thirty years in *gum san*.

"How does it feel to be a Canadian?" I ask.

"In China, this is the eighth month, the season of harvest." Then she adds: "The *Dai Pao* says that the old-age pension cheques will be increased by nine dollars next month."

As we walk home on this bright autumn morning, my mother clutches her piece of paper. Citizenship. She says she will go up to the cemetery and talk to my father this afternoon. She has something to tell him.

Heritage Day

◆ ◆ ◆

BY

BERT

ALMON

Under candy-striped tents in the park
national tables offer food and crafts
from the old countries
                                    Swedish pancakes
in cream, a Ukrainian woman using
wax and dye to create embroidered eggs
their intricate texture a reminder
we're all a happy mosaic here

But at the Chilean stand
there's a certain awkwardness
when people look at the wall hangings
the little cloth cut-outs
arranged in scenes from the homeland:
the secret police frisking a suspect
children eyeing a huge bottle of milk
impounded by a barbed wire fence
Some bits of the mosaic want to tell us
how they were formed in such jagged shapes
and in what ovens their enamel grew hard

Refugee

♦ ♦ ♦

BY

M.G.

VASSANJI

Furtively, he threw another quick glance at the reflection in the window across the aisle. Then a confirming, brooding stare at himself in the window beside him. Through the glass he peered outside at the passing scenery in the dark: ghostly trees and buildings, not a sign of life. When finally he sat back from the darkness, it took moments to adjust to the brightness inside.

There was nothing of interest in the compartment, just the rows of seats and people. Stops were few and far between on this train, passengers who entered and sat down were as quiet as those who got up and left. At one point a big man in a blue suit sat down heavily beside him, barely suppressing a grunt, glanced at him with a look of surprise and turned away to the aisle. Later the man brought out a magazine called *Kultur* and read it, still turned away. In reaction Karim confronted himself in the window yet again, then stared outside. A station flew past that the train ignored. He did not catch its name. It was this unpredictability that was the cause of his anxiety. He had been told to get off and change at Pegnitz.

He was, he had realised unhappily, dressed all wrong. He had bought the right kind of things, of course, and was wearing some of them. All according to fashions picked up from films, tourists, and foreign-returneds. His two sisters, who prided themselves in matters of fashion, had accompanied him shopping; his mother and father had approved his choice. Yet now in the bright light of this train compartment he stood out like a sore thumb, he thought, using an expression he had read from American novels.

No one that he had seen in the train wore sneakers, yet his stood out, sparkling white. His denim jeans were starchy like cardboard, and uncomfortable too. The sweater that in the store in Dar had appeared distinguished and conservative, now betrayed its faded grey, with the three large dirty red and white diamonds in front making pathetic attempts at design and colour. No wonder the first thing anyone looked at was his bright shoes then his face that needed a wash and shave. He looked, felt, so shrunken and small in this strange, alien environment. Alternately he sat forward; leaned back, pressing his arms onto the armrests; arched his back, stretched out his shoulders. He just wasn't right.

He had been instructed carefully. As soon as he got off the plane at Frankfurt not to speak to anybody but head straight for the immigration counters. If anyone came to ask him anything, to offer any help, he was to say only; "I am a refugee." To the immigration officers, the same thing: like a prayer. If anyone asked, "Have you come to look for work?" not to say yes or no, either way to fall into a trap, but to say only, "I am a refugee."

He had done just that.

He had got off the plane tired and dazed. The airport was radiant, busy, impressively modern, he expected nothing else. He had emerged into a large open area and paused uncertain: about him human traffic in all directions. He decided to follow a group of fellow-passengers, the wrong ones, apparently, for they soon walked under a lit sign that said TRANSIT. Avoid at all costs he had been told. He stopped, started back in the opposite direction. At that instant, it seemed, two men who had been standing together some distance away started heading towards him. They walked purposefully but without hurrying, their looks fixed on him. Like cowboys walk in movies, he thought fleetingly, as he looked around as if to escape; then he realised he couldn't avoid them and waited. They were the same height, not very tall, one in a dark and the other in a light blue suit, their hair...what will they do? He watched them come to a stop.

"Yes, can we help you?" They were standing not very close to him —at a little more than arm's length—but he felt crowded and without meaning to he took a step back but ran into his own bag and stumbled. One of the men leaned forward and took from him the passport he held and flipped the pages, in the process now coming to stand quite close to him.

"I am a refugee," Karim said.

They tried several questions including the one about work. He stuck to his guns: "I am a refugee."

The two men spoke briefly to each other, then started walking away with his passport, and Karim followed. He put his bag down and stopped when he saw a bank of clearly marked immigration counters to his right some distance away. But his interceptors walked on oblivious. He watched their backs, their unforced pace. Then one of them looked behind, and the other turned, and they stopped and looked at him for a moment. They walked back to him.

"I am a refugee," Karim said, somewhat defensively. There was a pause during which they eyed him reflectively. Then the man who held his passport smacked it with one hand against the other before, to Karim's surprise, handing it back to him. The two went sauntering towards the place where they had picked him up.

An immigration official made out some forms for him, stamped his passport, and gave him an address to report to. He was through.

Then the ordeal began. The few pounds and dollars he had come with he managed to have converted. He had just one telephone number with him, which he had learnt by heart, but he could not make the payphone work. Several times he had to yield it to other, impatient travellers. Minutes passed, he panicked: surely it was not this that was going to undo him? His rejected money tinkled back; the phone buzzed angrily at him; an efficient-sounding operator said something unintelligible to him. Desperately, yet half-heartedly he searched for a face he could trust. But who?

A man walked up to him. He was tall with a greying brown beard, wearing glasses, and grinning with big yellow teeth. His clothes were casual, a tweed jacket over woollen trousers, well used.

"You want to make a telephone call, yes?"

The boy was dumbfounded, alarmed.

"Yes, yes?" The man's insistence did not sound unfriendly though the grin, and the glinting glasses, and the tilt of his head as he spoke gave him a somewhat sinister look.

"I am a refugee."

"I know that. But you want to make a telephone call to a friend — perhaps a refugee like you — yes, yes?"

"I am a refugee."

"You are a refugee from where?"

He told him.

"Look, I have been to your country. Yes? I am not an immigration officer as you think. Nor am I a policeman."

He would not give the man the number he had been trying to call. He had heard too many stories of betrayal, arrived with too many warnings. They sat down and the man bought him coffee.

"I am waiting for someone," the man told him. "A writer, not a refugee. Yes?"

Karim nodded. He wondered what he should do. There was one telephone with instructions in English that he had barely tried before being ousted; surely he could make it work after a few more tries? Perhaps he could give someone — this man — a wrong number and learn how to use the phone! But no, if he made up another number he would forget the one he had learnt. That would finish him. He could go to town first...but suppose he got lost?

Suddenly the man looked up past him, intently, towards the arrival gate then got up breaking into a grin. Walking towards them was a rotund man with a beard, wearing a corduroy jacket. He looked like an Indian and he was carrying a small hold-all.

"I've got all your information," said the German, "except your flight number."

"Sorry, I forgot. Did you wait long?"

"No, no."

Karim was introduced to the Indian as the refugee. After a while, feeling rather foolish, he gave the two men the phone number. They talked, had more coffee and the German helped him make the telephone call. It was to a man called Anand in the city of Bayreuth. He was told to go to Bayreuth and given an address.

The German gave him a phone card and told him how to use it. He bought him his train ticket and told him he would have to change at Nurmburg. The train to Nurmburg was 20 minutes late and he might have to go to Pegnitz first and change for Bayreuth. But he should check with the conductor.

It was late afternoon and dusky when the train lurched forward taking him yet deeper into the alien country. The German had found his seat for him, the Indian had waited outside. The few hours of getting to the train station, the looking up of schedules and buying the ticket had been a lively frantic experience. Now left all by himself he began looking around him in the train. It was not very dark outside yet, and superimposed on the fleeting drab scenery outside the window he could just make out the constant but faint reflection of himself on it.

There was a sombreness in the compartment in spite of its brightness, a grim quietude. When he heard a voice it seemed as if it echoed from a distance. It felt eerie because he realised that the train did not move silently but with a steady rumble, which he had to strain to hear through the loud silence. Around him, everyone else sat composed into this stillness, belonging to it, until their stop came and they got up and left.

A conductor came by and clicked his ticket. "Bayreuth," he said, pointing at the ticket in his hand.

"Yes. Change at Pegnitz?" Karim asked.

The conductor gave him his ticket, saying a lot of words including "Bayreuth," and walked away.

Karim looked helplessly around him at the several people who had looked up, then went back to staring out the window.

He felt strange, preoccupied by an anxiety that allowed no other thoughts, even of home. His one objective was to get himself and his two bags to Bayreuth. There, a phone call or a taxi.

A station came with a name in large letters and "Bayreuth" in smaller. Obviously this was not Bayreuth. Why put two names to confuse foreigners like him?

Finally PEGNITZ in large letters and some people got up. But he had to be sure. He looked at his neighbour.

"Excuse me, sir. Is this Pegnitz?"

He had to clear his throat and repeat.

The man leaned towards the window and gave a quick look outside. "Ja. Pegnitz."

The boy hurried out, pulling his suitcase, the hold-all over his shoulder.

The train disappeared and the station cleared of everyone except him, of all sound except his shuffling. It was overwhelmingly dark. Not a soul, he thought, isn't anyone else going to Bayreuth?...With a sinking feeling he realised that the train which had just pulled out was on its way to Bayreuth. That's what the conductor must have said.

Wearily he put his suitcase down against a wall and sat on it. The night was thick with mist. Overhead a sharp silvery half moon sliced through scattered clouds. In the distance, the lights of a town — like somewhere far away — and cars. But not a sound. If something happened to him, if his throat were slit in this godforsaken place, if he met a ghost or a vampire, no one would know. How stupid, he thought, to venture out like this into the unknown. But he had been pushed out, ever so gently. From a sitting-room full of family in Dar into this utter, utter loneliness under an alien sky.

There was a time, not many years ago, when a bread cart would go creaking down Uhuru Street, pulled by one man in front, pushed by another at the back. It would stop at the street corners and boys or servants would run up and buy bread for the evening or the following morning. Hot steaming loaves huddled in the cart under a green tarpaulin cover. Often at his home they had bread and butter for supper, with sweet creamy tea.

Now there were daily queues for bread and sugar; milk came in packets from the new factory, diluted, sometimes sour. There were rumours that boys would be recruited to fight Idi Amin, the tyrant to the north. And others that Amin would send planes to bomb Dar.

The body of an Asian woman had been found on a beach, mutilated, hanging from a tree. Another, an elderly widow, had been hacked to death by robbers in her flat.

Three times his family's application for immigration to Canada had been rejected. For all three failures his mother and two sisters blamed their father. They were right, his father simply didn't have the heart to pack up his life and move to a cold climate. At each interview he blurted out something that was obviously inappropriate, that raised the interviewer's eyebrows and made the rest of them squirm. Each time though, he had a plausible explanation. After the last interview, when they returned home once more without "medicals," there had been the biggest row. As usual they were in his parents' bedroom that was also the sitting room. His mother was sitting on the bed, braced for the quarrel, his father — resigned to it — was fiddling with the telephone as if unsure whether to make a call or not.

"You didn't have to tell the man that you keep money ready for the robbers — that you joke with them: 'Business is bad, next time there will be more' ... "

"I thought he would like it — think I'm good-natured or something."

"*Good natured.* A fool more likely. You could see the expression on the man's face."

"The young punk. Come to sit in judgement on us. You know why there is no bread? The Canadians brought a new machine for baking bread at the state bakery. Throw away the old ones they said. Automatic! Well, the machine's broken and there are no parts. Meanwhile someone in Canada's made a bundle. Canadian aid!"

"You've been listening to that socialist again!" His mother practically screamed.

"Shiraz's a clever chap."

Once more Shiraz Uncle's name entered the home like an evil spell bringing disruption. His father seemed to sense this as soon as he had uttered the name. Shiraz Uncle was his father's educated sister's even more educated husband, and reputedly a supporter of government policies. At the mere mention of his name, Karim's mother's face would contort with rage. Already she was getting flushed and breathless, bosom heaving, searching for words. Sometimes in such a state she got up and went to the kitchen where Karim's two sisters would join her. This time she exploded, pounding her chest twice, saying "I die! I die!" and weeping forcefully, at which point both his sisters started wailing. His father, who thought he had successfully waylaid his wife's querulousness with good humour and a change of subject, was caught off balance.

"What, now?" he began in embarrassment, and looked towards his son to see if even he had resorted to tears.

It was then that the telephone rang, shrilly cutting into the scene, startling most of all his father who was standing next to it.

An operator at the phone exchange had been bribed so his mother could talk long-distance with her family. This was after she kept on complaining about how difficult it was for them to make long-distance calls and how easy for those in Canada. They had a television now, although there was no local TV station and they had to make do with poor reception from Zanzibar. His father even got hold of smuggled foreign goods like cellophone wrapping and soft "squeezable" toilet tissue and Kleenex. And Avon beauty products for his mother and sisters who in mosque came to be called the Avon ladies.

"Oh the hell we live in!" sobbed his mother over the phone. Her face was wet with the copious tears dripping off her chubby cheeks. At the other end of the line a hushing, comforting voice was just audible. It was usually her brother who called, to whom she was close. After a while his father spoke on the phone, receiving a good ticking off, finally getting furious: "Call her back if you want to!"

Then surprisingly, like the end of a storm, calmness returned as if nothing had happened and that night they could hear their mother and father talking in barely controlled husky tones in the other room.

His sisters had studied shorthand, typing, bookkeeping and anything else available and were now simply idling, reading Mills & Boon love stories or helping around while waiting to be taken to Canada.

The happiest times in Karim's life had been when one of his other uncles, his father's brother, had returned with his family from Pakistan after a miserable time there. There had followed happy years, with two families, seven children, living together in adjacent flats. Then his uncle's eldest son who was in Canada sponsored his family; it was only a year since they had left.

His intellectual uncle, Shiraz, had no intention of going to live anywhere else. In fact the government itself sent him abroad several times and Shiraz Uncle always returned, happy to be back, for which many regarded him a socialist fool. But it was Shiraz Uncle who, on returning from Germany recently, told his father of a way to send his son abroad.

"If you want to send him, this is one way, but I don't see why you want to or what's the hurry."

"I don't think I'll do it," said his father. "Karim's never been away. I don't think he'll want to go in that manner. What do you think, Karim?"

Karim was the only other person in the shop, and said, "No, I don't want to go like that." His father was right. He couldn't bear the thought of separation. And his uncle spoke of an indirect route through Germany, where he didn't know a soul.

But that evening Karim mentioned the possibility briefly to his mother and sisters, as a novelty, an idea typical of his crazy uncle. But they jumped on it, never letting go for an instant, and he was overwhelmed.

"Your father's no good, you be the man now. God will preserve you. Think of your sisters. Do it for them."

He had no choice. His silence — brought on by his mother's tender words of solicitation, her trust, her hand on his brow, her quivering lips, her sweet Avon smell — was taken for assent, and they were joyfully discussing the details of his trip when his father entered the room. His mother looked up at her husband in triumph, his sister Yasmin said joyfully, "Karim says he'll go to Germany."

Karim looked at him, expressionless. For the first time his father looked beaten.

A warm bright light was shining on his face, making him aware of his unwashed face, sticky neck. "Polizei" was a German word he understood and the light moved up to a spot above him as a kindness. After some moments he could see the two policemen who were looking at him, telling things to him and to each other. They were quite young and he thought one was perhaps even younger than him.

"Bayreuth," he said and it seemed that they were walking away, leaving him alone, but they turned and spoke and the younger one came up to him and gestured for him to pick up his bags.

"We go. Police station."

His heart sank. So be it then. He had been so dispirited, and now, woken up from a dream about home into this bleak deserted train station, he felt terribly depressed. And a trace relieved even at the thought that he would be sent back home.

They drove him to a square brick building which was the police station, walked him to a room at the back that had a table in the middle and some chairs. The door clicked shut behind him and he realized that it was probably unlocked. He sat down on a chair, lay his head sideways on the table between his arms and slept as he had often done out of exhaustion in school.

He was woken up by the sound of a chair scraping the floor. A middle-aged plump woman was wiping the floor with a mop. He watched for a while in amazement. From time to time she glanced at him. After that chore, she began wiping the window panes meticulously. He thought he had never seen anyone wiping window panes before. The room was chilly, the woman was wearing a sweater. The sun was shining brilliantly outside, somewhere, but not entering the room.

When he stood up, uncertainly, the woman left the room in a hurry, closing the door behind her. A policeman walked in; not one of the two who had picked him up last night: this one was older and plumper, balding. The policeman accompanied him to the washroom. Karim did nothing but stare at himself for a while in the mirror: he felt dull, out of touch with the face looking at him. Not the face he woke up with each morning, excited about the day, taking his time shaving and bathing despite his sisters' pleas to vacate the bathroom, singing joyously…If the policeman standing at the door had told him that it was not his face but that of someone else behind him, he would have believed it. Wearily he went back to the room. Two men in civilian clothes were waiting for him. They gave him coffee, examined his passport, began questioning.

This time he readily relinquished the phone number in Bayreuth, and the address. He did not care any more: he did not want to lie, to resist, to stay whatever the cost. He would gladly go back knowing he had tried. The only thing that nagged at him was the thought he had betrayed the men in Bayreuth who had offered to help him. He asked the two officers if he could call Bayreuth to tell them where he was but they smiled.

The men drove him to Bayreuth. Clouds were in motion above, and it was intermittently sunny; the road was a clear grey ribbon in front of them, cutting through greenery in a scene that could have come out of a story book. He wondered if *Heidi* was set in these parts. Perhaps *The Sound of Music?* It all seemed unreal, he could very well be dreaming. They entered town and after a while parked beside some blocks of flats.

On their way to the eighth floor in the last building, Karim wondered if this was really the end, the whole immigration ring to be arrested thanks to him. With trepidation and curiosity and feeling above all like a schoolboy being accompanied to the headmaster's office, he walked between the men who eventually stopped outside a door and knocked stiffly.

There was a short interval and the sounds of some fumbling at the door, after which it was opened, wide, releasing a blast of food smells that stunned him. Karim was gently pushed in by the elbow and had to step over a towel on the floor. There were three men and a woman in the flat. One of the men was an African, from Nigeria, and he was at the piano. The woman was German. Of the two remaining men, one was from Sri Lanka — Anand, his host — and the other from India. All with papers in order. To Karim the room exuded a homely warmth that was as comforting as an embrace. He wondered how the smell of the cooking had been kept inside, then saw the wet towel that had been used to block the space under the door. The two officers were invited to look inside in the bedrooms and they did. After a peek in the kitchen, they left.

When the two men had been seen to have driven off, pandemonium broke loose around him. The door burst open and five more people — four men and a woman who had been hiding in a German neighbour's flat it appeared — stormed in. And the guest became the centre of attention. Everyone seemed to be speaking at once, asking him questions, skipping his answers, offering advice. They told him not to worry...or to start worrying...What happened at the airport? they asked, how did the officers get hold of him? what answers did he give? ...The woman, her face so close to him he could smell her perfume, was telling him, "...this is Bavaria. Big feet. Leather aprons. You know? Yodelei-o. Hitler started off here you know... "

He didn't know. "Wagner, Wagner, Wagner," said the German neighbour and started walking stiffly about the room singing in a bass voice. The second woman had one of her legs on the arm of a sofa and acknowledged Karim's glance with a smile. The Nigerian had started playing the piano. The Indian was walking around looking at wall hangings. A plate was thrust in Karim's hand, he was escorted to the kitchen. Anand was telling him how he could go to Canada via Hamburg.

"You will be let off in a boat some miles from the coast. Throw away your passport. Say you are from Lebanon. Beirut…Don't worry. The Canadians can't tell the difference yet. But there is some risk involved, and some money… "

Illegals: Shadows in the Underground

◆ ◆ ◆

BY

MARINA JIMINEZ

AND

CORINNA SCHULER

Alberto stares at papers strewn on his living room floor, stuffing hanging from a knifed couch, broken glass, ripped books. Ransacked! They're after him. It's Mendoza, Argentina, 1988. He suspects it's the work of the military, the military he's protested against for years.

Alberto had known it was risky. It's dangerous to demonstrate for human rights, join a populist political party, and plaster anti-military posters around town.

But he did it anyway, marching through the streets and attending left-wing party meetings throughout the 1980s. He can't forget the many friends killed by army officers, the thousands who "disappeared" during his country's infamous dirty war from 1976 to 1982.

There have already been threats. And a terrible beating, when soldiers smashed his teeth with a rifle butt.

But now they are tearing apart his home. He has to get out, fast.

Stomach in knots, Alberto flees from one safe house to the next, running for his life.

Finally, with the help of friends, he gets a ticket to safety.

The plane lands at Montreal's Mirabel airport on a freezing Christmas Eve, 1988. He breathes easier as he steps onto Canadian soil. But the 33-year-old fidgets in his beige pants and dark suit as he stands in line to face a new fear: Canada Immigration.

The officer asks through an interpreter: "Where are you going? Are you here to visit or to stay?"

Everyone arriving in Canada has a right to make a refugee claim, but Alberto is too scared to tell the truth now. They'll send him home, he fears.

"I'm going to Edmonton to visit my aunt," he answers, clutching a small suitcase with the only things he'd had time to grab: three shirts, a sweater, a few toiletries.

"I came for the Christmas holidays."

That's the first lie. He'll have to tell many more as he slips into the shadows of the underground where illegals hide.

◆ ◆ ◆

Alberto dunks the mop in water and scrubs grungy tiles. The toilets stink of ammonia. He rubs his back and tries to ignore the callouses that sting his hands. He's tired of working seven days a week, seven hours a day.

Tears fall down his pudgy cheeks as he thinks of what he's left behind: his job as a shoe salesman, his dreams of becoming an architect, his family's love, the Argentine sunshine.

"I cried of frustration," he recalls later. "The solitude, the loneliness. I had no one to talk to, only my mop…. I was completely alone."

Alberto has been emptying ashtrays and scrubbing Edmonton malls almost three years now. He got a job with a local janitorial company months after arriving in Edmonton.

At work he uses an alias: he concocted the name "Luis Bernal" using his own middle name and a friend's surname. He gets paid in cash, under the table. He can't use his uncle's social insurance number anymore. Using the number made things smoother, but his uncle would only lend it out for a month fearing he'd be stuck paying extra income tax.

Mothers of missing Argentinians march at Plaza de Mayo, Buenos Aires, 1982.

Alberto works hard, but saves little. He says the boss often pays late and not the full amount promised. But he can't argue. Illegals have no rights.

Latin American friends sympathize and many allow him to stay in their apartments. He moves from place to place but never gets his own room. He sleeps on a thin mattress, having nightmares about home. He dreams of the day Argentine soldiers nabbed him at a demonstration and kicked him down with their steel-toed boots. He can't sleep with the window open: noise outside frightens him.

He's even scared of a trip to the doctor. His leg is sore and he's limping but it takes weeks before he dares ask a friend to lend him his Alberta health care card. Alberto feels lucky when the nurse jots the number on a file without question.

"It's very ugly because you have to live hidden. You think that everyone who looks at you will arrest you. You always have fear."

Deep down, Alberto knows it can't last. Canada Immigration is out there. Eventually someone will rat.

◆ ◆ ◆

"Alberto! Wake up!" Carlos whispers urgently in Spanish. Carlos, Alberto's latest roommate, shakes him out of a sound sleep.

"Get up," Carlos says. "I have something important to tell you."

RCMP and immigration officers are looking for Alberto. Moments earlier, they had confronted Carlos in the apartment hallway, asking about Luis Bernal.

"He's gone downtown," Carlos lied, slipping inside to warn Alberto as soon as the officers left.

But the police will be back. They know where Alberto lives, they know his false name, they know he works illegally.

For years he'd thought about this moment, dreading it. Now it's arrived, but Alberto still doesn't know what to do.

"On the one hand, I felt calm," he says later. "On the other hand, I felt nervous about the thought of returning to Argentina."

He must decide what to do. Should he run? Should he stay? He discusses the question with his friend while stuffing his only possessions into a hockey bag: a tape recorder, cassettes, books and clothing.

Time ticks. He can't eat. Then, a knock at the door. RCMP. He doesn't try to hide. It's all over.

◆ ◆ ◆

It's been just two months since the arrest, but already Alberto's life in the underground seems a thousand years ago.

Everything has changed.

"Whoever (tipped off the RCMP) thought he was doing something bad to me but, in the end, he did something good," Alberto tells two reporters at the west-end apartment where he still lives with Carlos.

He has a work permit now, granted after he passed his first refugee hearing at immigration.

He smiles sheepishly as he proudly hands reporters his ID badge from the Provincial Museum. Still a janitor, but this time Alberto's real name is on the badge. Now he gets weekends off, and a genuine pay cheque.

The day of his final hearing before the Immigration and Refugee Board, Alberto slicks back his black hair, puts on a pressed navy suit and polished shoes. He wants to make a good impression.

He knows it will be weeks before they decide his case, but he's praying the two adjudicators assigned to hear his refugee claim will believe the story.

Thoughts of returning to Argentina frighten him. Who will care if the military returns to get him, if he disappears?

"I am just a little guy, a grain of sand," he says.

Alberto walks into the hearing room, the door closes behind.

His life is in their hands.

For two months, Alberto watches the mail for a decision. He can think of nothing else.

Word came Friday. He can scarcely believe it. The board has accepted his refugee claim. He can stay.

"I'm left without words," he says, his hands trembling. "Now, I can plan my future, live without worry."

He has his life back.

Beyond the Sea

♦ ♦ ♦

BY

NICK

LEES

The teenagers didn't flinch when they found the path to happiness and marriage lay across the storm-ravaged Gulf of Tonkin.

Trung Lam and his sweetheart Le An (pronounced Lee-Ann) were nearly drowned in 1980 when they fled Hanoi in a small boat. They spent 45 days at sea.

"We will celebrate our 10th wedding anniversary this year," says Trung, 32, who is studying education at the University of Alberta and works as a gas pump jockey on weekends.

Trung says they: "did the right thing in leaving Vietnam. But I don't think either of us would again risk our lives at sea."

The Lams now have two children, eight-year-old Angela and six-year-old Brian, both good students at Alex Taylor Elementary School.

Family finances are such that Angela takes piano lessons and teaches her father what she has learnt and he then teaches Brian.

"Edmonton is so different from the world in which we grew up," says Le An, 31, who is upgrading her education at the Alberta Vocational College before studying accounting.

Le An was six when the Americans first bombed Hanoi, a river port, railroad and industrial centre with a population of 2.5 million.

"The women and children were evacuated and stayed with families in the country, where there was no electricity and running water," she says.

Trung remembers the bombs falling in 1966 and 1972 and how air raid sirens would send men running to underground shelters. And he remembers razed buildings and firefighters struggling to help the trapped.

The third eldest son in a family of 10, Trung says he didn't finish school in a classless society that placed no value on education, for most people were destined to toil in factories. He worked in his father's optician's business.

"Life wasn't dissimilar to that of the Soviets now," says Trung. "There were always shortages and line-ups at stores. But the worst thing was the Communist indoctrination. There were speakers on the streets that constantly gave you lopsided views. Everything was censored and strict. You couldn't read the books you wanted to."

Trung and Le An met when he was 16. They enjoyed one another's company and spent time sitting under trees by the river, chatting and dreaming.

It was Trung's father who convinced him he should flee and arranged with Le An's uncle for her to leave. Her parents—her father is a chemical engineer—didn't know until later that she had gone. "It would have been so hard for them to see me go," she says.

Lam Sr. paid 2.5 ounces of gold for each of their passages on a sail-powered fishing boat that measured little more than four metres in length and carried 14 people.

The couple made the trip to Haiphong by bus and innocently embarked on the Hong Kong-bound sailboat.

"When there was no wind, we would paddle," says Trung. "At other times, the sea poured into the boat and we were constantly bailing."

It was near the end of their voyage that one night they were engulfed by a severe thunderstorm:

"We had no radio and were very afraid," says Trung. "Fortunately, a Chinese fishing boat spotted us and towed us to safety."

In Hong Kong, the couple lived in one of several huge refugee camps for one year while seeking clearance to a western country. Trung made toys, worked as a welder and cobbler, while Le An helped make radios and computer chips.

"We were asked to name three countries we'd like to live in and nearly everyone selected the U.S. or Canada," says Trung.

Not speaking a word of English, the couple flew into Ottawa—they promised the Canadian government they would pay back their fares—and were met by two ladies who held up a card with their names written in Vietnamese.

"We communicated with sign language while we learnt English at school," says Trung. "We lived with one of the women and her husband, a government worker, outside Ottawa for seven months before getting our own place.

"We will be forever grateful to those people. We still write and call them."

Trung was paid $3 an hour for his work as a cleaner and

automotive partsman, while Le An received $250 a month from the same auto dealer for household chores and looking after his children.

"I was very shy and spoke few words of English," says Le An. "It was only later that I realized I had been taken advantage of."

But there was good news. Trung's father had made it to Edmonton in 1981 with the rest of his family and the couple came here to join them.

Trung worked for an upholstery company for a few months before joining *The Journal* as press room attendant (cleaner) in 1981, a job he held for eight years. In future, he would like to work as a teacher or social worker.

His wife worked for an hotel's housekeeping department before taking time off to begin a family. In 1989, she worked as a parking lot attendant for six months before returning to school.

"If I study, I know I can get a good, well-paid job," says Le An, who spends what free time she has helping with community fund raisers, often singing. She also likes to read the classics and counts Victor Hugo among her favorites.

"We eventually plan to move from our apartment to our own home," she says. "When we are both working again, we will save for a down payment. In Hanoi, our prospects were never good. There was always poverty and hunger."

Daughter Angela takes ballet lessons and recently passed a Royal Conservatory of Music piano exam with honors.

Brian wants to learn Kung Fu.

Dad rises at 5 a.m. and tutors both children with school work. Their television hours are rationed, but Trung supplements their entertainment by reading traditional Oriental stories at bedtime.

"He also finds time to come to our school as a volunteer to help tutor," says Alex Taylor principal Steve Ransankar. "He's a talented teacher."

During his early days in Canada, Trung was impressed when he saw a workman reading a newspaper.

"I thought maybe in 100 years I would be able to do that. Now I am reading philosophy at the university level."

Involvement Overcomes Isolation

♦ ♦ ♦

BY

LESLEY FRANCIS

The door opens. The welcome begins. The Quaidoos almost sweep you in the door. Off with your coat, hat, and gloves. Their home is your home.

"If you wanted to know about family we should have sat down to dinner," says Peter, 43.

"Yeah, African food," laughs Esther, 40.

This warmth and openness is one of the legacies the family brought here from Ghana, their country of birth, where society is more close-knit and more relaxed than in Canada. A typical day means taking time to hang loose with family and friends. No gilt-edged invitations. No phone calls to see if anyone's home.

"You just drop by," says Esther.

Everyone takes care of the other. If you have to work, there's always someone around to keep an eye on your kids. Forget hiring a babysitter.

It's something they miss living in Canada. Life here is a lot more isolated unless you make the effort to be a part of what's going on, says Peter. So, their solution has been to just jump in wholeheartedly.

And it's stood them in good stead, perhaps even been their salvation, since they came to Canada a little more than 16 years ago. They landed in Saskatoon on Sept. 4, 1975 and immediately found themselves culturally, geographically and emotionally isolated.

They didn't know anyone. There were almost no other black families in Saskatoon. They weren't prepared for the weather. Their families were half a world away. And Esther was at home with Justin, then three years old.

"I cried for four months," Esther remembers. "I wanted to go home. I told Peter, 'I can't stay here. It's too hard.' We were really close to our families so the separation was difficult."

They got involved in their community and their church. Still, it took Esther four years to finally adjust to Canada while

Peter managed to do it in a little more than two years, probably because being in the work force made it easier for him to achieve a sense of connection.

Today, they are not unlike many other Canadian families. Peter and Esther work hard—he's a maintenance technician, she's a hairdresser. They have lived in this house on a typical Edmonton street since they moved here in 1980.

The Quaidoos belong to their community league. And each of their four children plays sports. In fact, Justin, now 19, was a top ball player on Harry Ainlay's football team.

And, like so many other parents, Peter and Esther have to contend with a generation of kids who are always asking questions and insisting on the power to contribute to the decision-making process.

It's not something they are familiar with. In Ghana, Mom and Dad's word is law, says Esther. It is obeyed without question: here, more flexible child-rearing is necessary with their children—Justin, Frank, 15, Irene, 11, and Hal, 7.

Peter and Esther came in search of a better life for themselves and their children. And they haven't been disappointed. Well, not if you don't count the weather.

"The weather was difficult for us," explains Peter. "That first year it started snowing in October. But, it's not something that would have driven us away. Choosing a country is like choosing a partner. You aren't going to like everything about it, but that's no reason not to live there."

As they look back at the obstacles they've tackled, Peter and Esther feel they were minor. Although they'd describe Canadians as a little less open to anything outside their realm of experience, they've never had to contend with any major examples of discrimination.

"The kids have probably had a little more trouble than we have, mostly at school," Esther explains. "But, if I thought about everything that could have been taken as discrimination, I'd have a huge, continuous migraine. Our policy is to forgive and forget."

Some part of their hearts remains permanently in Ghana. Not necessarily because of the country itself or the kind of life they had when they still lived there, but because they have been unable to get any of their family members into Canada.

"If we need help, no one's here we can really count on," Esther says. "And we aren't there for them. So some part of my mind is always on them and what's happening to them."

Part of the family ethic in Ghana is that those in the family who have, have to take care of those who have not. Peter and Esther know they are doing much better than his three brothers and three sisters or her two sisters.

"This makes it difficult in our own personal decision making," says Peter who's been back to Ghana four times. Esther's been three times and the kids twice. "They don't have too many material things, like cars. Their basic needs are being met, but the economic situation isn't great because of inflation. I have sent money home to help when they've asked."

Esther and Peter make sure Justin, Frank, Irene and Hal know about their cultural heritage. They still speak *Akan,* the most common dialect in Ghana which is actually a combination of five other languages, to the kids.

The kids also dress in costume and learn songs, stories and games common to Ghana. Peter is on the executive of the Ghana Friendship Association which is now made up of 40 to 50 families. In 1980, there were fewer than 15 families.

"We've taught our children to respect the people they meet, to respect different cultures," says Peter. "We all have something to offer. If we get to know each other better, we can minimize confrontations. We can mix, we can learn. Once we all understand and accept what other cultures have, we'll be able to see how beautiful the world is."

Peter carries out his philosophy personally, dropping in to visit other cultural groups when he has the time. And he's always been well received, he says.

"I don't wait for an invitation. I just show up. I've dropped in on Jewish groups, Ukrainian groups, even Scottish groups.

"It's up to each individual to get involved, so we can bridge the isolation."

Becoming a Multicultural Society

My Hands

BY TAKEO NAKANO

My hands tremble
As I sign my naturalization papers
Making me a Canadian citizen
And Canada my final resting place.

from Canada's Original Immigration Act

"26. No immigrant shall be permitted to land in Canada, who is feeble-minded, an idiot, or an epileptic, or who is insane, or who has had an attack of insanity within five years; nor shall any immigrant be so landed who is deaf and dumb, blind or infirm, unless he belongs to a family accompanying him or already in Canada, and which gives security, satisfactory to the Minister, and in conformity with the regulations in that behalf, if any, for his permanent support if admitted into Canada.
"27. No immigrant shall be permitted to land in Canada who is afflicted with a loathsome disease, or with a disease which is contagious or infectious, and which may become dangerous to the public health or widely disseminated, whether such immigrant intends to settle in Canada or only to pass through Canada to settle in some other country; provided that if such disease is one which is curable within a reasonably

short time, the immigrant suffering therefrom may, subject to the regulations in that behalf, if any, be permitted to remain on board where hospital facilities do not exist on shore, or to leave the vessel for medical treatment, under such regulations as may be made by the Minister. "28. No person shall be permitted to land in Canada who is a pauper, or destitute, a professional beggar, or vagrant, or who is likely to become a public charge; and any person landed in Canada who, within two years thereafter, has become a charge upon the public funds, whether municipal, provincial, or federal, or an inmate…"

Canada is a Garden

BY THE RIGHT HONOURABLE
JOHN G. DIEFENBAKER, 1961

"Canada is a garden…into which has been transplanted the hardiest and brightest flowers of many lands, each retaining in its new environment the best of the qualities for which it was loved and prized in its native lands…"

from
The Multiculturalism
Policy of Canada

3. (1) It is hereby declared to be the policy of the Government of Canada to

(a) recognize and promote the understanding that multiculturalism reflects the cultural and racial diversity of Canadian society and acknowledges the freedom of all members of Canadian society to preserve, enhance and share their cultural heritage;

(b) recognize and promote the understanding that multiculturalism is a fundamental characteristic of the Canadian heritage and identity and that it provides an invaluable resource in the shaping of Canada's future;

(c) promote the full and equitable participation of individuals and communities of all origins in the continuing evolution and shaping of all aspects of Canadian society and assist them in the elimination of any barrier to such participation;

(d) recognize the existence of communities whose members share a common origin and their historic contribution to Canadian society, and enhance their development;

(e) ensure that all individuals receive equal treatment and equal protection under the law, while respecting and valuing their diversity;

(f) encourage and assist the social, cultural, economic and political institutions of Canada to be both respectful and inclusive of Canada's multicultural character;

(g) promote the understanding and creativity that arise from the interaction between individuals and communities of different origins;

(h) foster the recognition and appreciation of the diverse cultures of Canadian society and promote the reflection and the evolving expressions of those cultures;

(i) preserve and enhance the use of languages other than English and French, while strengthening the status and use of the official languages of Canada; and

(j) advance multiculturalism throughout Canada in harmony with the national commitment to the official languages of Canada.

(2) It is further declared to be the policy of the Government of Canada that all federal institutions shall

(a) ensure that Canadians of all origins have an equal opportunity to obtain employment and advancement in those institutions;

(b) promote policies, programs and practices that enhance the ability of individuals and communities of all origins to contribute to the continuing evolution of Canada;

(c) promote policies, programs and practices that enhance the understanding of and respect for the diversity of the members of Canadian society;

(d) collect statistical data in order to enable the development of policies, programs and practices that are sensitive and responsive to the multicultural reality of Canada;

(e) make use, as appropriate, of the language skills and cultural understanding of individuals of all origins; and

(f) generally, carry on their activities in a manner that is sensitive and responsive to the multicultural reality of Canada.

Youth Our Best Hope to End Racial Discrimination

◆ ◆ ◆

BY GERRY WEINER

If I think back to my early years, what I remember most of all is the tremendous optimism I felt about the future. As I stared out of the window of my parents' home in the heart of Montreal's inner city, the world outside seemed to be filled with adventure and opportunity. I felt that if I worked very hard and applied myself, little could stand in the way of my aspirations.

Well, in many ways I was right.

But there were also times when I realized that life wasn't quite so simple.

I grew up in a Jewish household that was very supportive. Yet I was never sheltered from the knowledge that there were people outside that safe haven—people I had never even met—who held misconceptions about me and my family, and about the community to which I belonged.

I remember what it was like back then to come face to face with prejudice even on those very streets that were so familiar to me.

Today, years later, prejudice, bigotry, and racism continue to make the pursuit of a full and rewarding life a real struggle for many Canadians. They are denied a sense of their rightful place and a feeling of belonging. They are robbed of their dignity and self-respect, and feel that "social justice" and "equality" are mere words. Little more.

Today we acknowledge their struggle. On this March 21st, 1990, communities throughout Canada and around the world affirm a fundamental ideal that is at the heart of our humanity. It is an ideal that has persisted over time and across geographical barriers, regardless of those who would try to suppress it; an ideal fortified in the human resolve for justice and fairness. It is our passionate belief in the equality of all people, and our reasoned rejection of any form of prejudice on the basis of the color of one's skin, country of origin, cultural tradition, or any other external difference between one human being and another.

That is why we are here today on Parliament Hill. That is why, at this moment, events are taking place in cities and towns all across Canada, in schools and places of worship, in community organizations and in government offices. We are joining the nations of the world in marking this International Day for the Elimination of Racism and Racial Discrimination.

Some may ask why a handful of Canada's youth have been asked to participate in a special way on this day of public awareness. After all, adults perpetuate these hurtful and often degrading attitudes. Surely they can resolve their own problems.

My response is quite simple, really. I believe that in this area the adult world is in need of the leadership of youth. And I also believe that now is the time to let Canada's young people to help realize a new and better destiny for Canada.

There is an energy and enthusiasm that is as irrepressible as it is undeniable among our youth. They are untainted by pragmatism. They do not accept injustice as a "natural" part of everyday life. Instead, the world that adults have made is seen with remarkable clarity through their comprehending eyes.

Young Canadians do not have a blind faith in our future but a positive one. Yes, they see the external differences among us. But they see our diversity as far more interesting and exciting than sameness. They understand that we're all Canadians. We all have an equal stake in our future. And each of us has a right to participate and share that future. Canadian youth are able to see beyond the bent and twisted creed of racism and develop their own moral code by which to guide their actions.

When I look out onto this gathering I know that the young people in this room are certainly no exception. Each of you has already demonstrated leadership in your communities and excellence in your schools. You have proven just how much young people can contribute today, as well as your leadership potential in the years ahead. You have done so because you recognize that an enormous array of challenges exist out there, outside of these elegant surroundings.

I'm sure you have been told on many occasions that the youth of today are our future. I say all the more reason why you cannot be absolved from the present. Every day in this country there are terrible injustices which we must all address collectively.

Our daily newspapers are filled with these disturbing headlines: "Up to one-third of Canadians may be bigots"…"Natives repeatedly hit by racism"…"Sale of racist pins flourishes"…"Turbaned Sikhs not welcome under any circumstances"…and…"Anti-semitic acts on the rise."

These captions represent only a sample of where we are and how much work we have yet to do.

We are all aware that racism is a very complex problem that has afflicted our institutions and our interaction as a society. But what is it like to be on the receiving end, to be the object of that hatred?

For the victim, all this complexity boils down to a way of feeling.

When students are ridiculed in the school yard—simply because of the color of their skin or racial features—they come to know a terrible feeling. One that they will never be able to shake completely. It is a feeling of hopelessness that returns when they find out they didn't get the job they were qualified for because they didn't fit the so-called "corporate image." It is a feeling of anger and frustration when they hear about an apartment that is for rent but are told upon arriving that there are no vacancies. It is a feeling of isolation when they are the last to be served at a crowded store counter, and only then with disrespect. And certainly, it is a feeling most deeply felt when their own children experience the cruelty of racism for the first time. Then, it is almost unbearable.

For the victim, prejudice does more than hurt feelings, it wounds to the very core.

Of course, there is an overwhelming question we have to ask ourselves: why should generation after generation of Canadians have to cope with this kind of oppression?

I have talked to young people about these problems and I've discovered that they are acutely aware of what is going on. They are not short on ideas about how we can improve the lives and well-being of all Canadians, how we can help to understand each other better. Our young people understand that leadership in the fight against racism and racial discrimination is not about conformity. It's about individualism, the kind that can overcome the temptation to "follow the crowd." It means accepting the risk that some of your peers will disapprove when you challenge their prejudices. It is true, there are risks involved whenever any one of us stands up for the victims of racism.

Yet moral courage, founded on idealism and expressed through concrete actions, is an essential quality of all our finest leaders. And it is not a coincidence that moral courage is at the very heart of progress and change.

Although the actions we take during the course of our lives may seem undramatic and maybe even insignificant at times, it is the sum total of our actions that will rewrite those headlines, that will eradicate racism from our society and fan the fires of progress and change.

You and your peers will carry forward the vision of this March 21st and in the ones to follow. With a commitment to action and to integrity, you can make a better Canada.

That is my appeal to our young leaders and to everyone who is capable of thinking young. Make this generation and the next a victory for justice and true equality.

It is the right way for us to live as Canadians.

It is the only way—together.

We Must Have Dreams

◆ ◆ ◆

BY

JOHN

AMAGOALIK

Will the Inuit disappear from the face of this earth? Will we become extinct? Will our culture, our language and our attachment to nature be remembered only in history books? These questions bring a great sadness to me. To realize that we Inuit are in the same category as the great whales, the bald eagle, the husky and the polar bear brings me great fear. To realize that our people can be classified as an endangered species is very disturbing. Is our culture like a wounded polar bear that has gone out to sea to die alone? What can be done? There does not seem to be one single answer to these questions.

It may be true that the physical part of our culture has been eroded to the point where it can never return to its full potential. But the non-physical part of our culture — our attitude towards life, our respect for nature, our realization that others will follow who deserve the respect and concern of present generations — are deeply entrenched within ourselves. The presence of our ancestors within ourselves is very strong. The will to survive is there. This part of our culture will die a slow death, if it ever dies at all. If we are to survive as a race, we must have the understanding and patience of the dominant cultures of this country. We do not need the pity, the welfare, the paternalism and the colonialism which has been heaped upon us over the years.

We must teach our children their mother tongue. We must teach them what they are and where they came from. We must teach them the values which have guided our society over the thousands of years. We must teach them our philosophies which go back beyond the human memory. We must keep the embers burning from the fires which used to burn in our villages so that we may gather around them again. It is this spirit we must keep alive so that it may guide us again in a new life in a changed world. Who is responsible for keeping this spirit alive? It is clearly the older people. We must have the leadership which they once provided us. They must realize this responsibility and accept it. If the older people will remember, the young must listen.

In a world which becomes more complicated with each passing year, we must rely on the simple, gentle ways of our people to guide us. In a world so full of greed, we must share. We must remember that, of all the things in this world, nothing belongs to us. Of what we take, we must share.

A lot of people tell me that we must forget the past, and instead, look to the future. To me it would be a mistake to completely ignore the past because the past determines the present and the present determines what will be in the future. Sometimes it is necessary to look to the past to make decisions about the future. When I talk about the future and try to describe what I would like for my children, some people sometimes say to me that I am only dreaming. What is wrong with dreaming? Sometimes dreams come true, if only one is determined enough. What kind of world would we live in if people did not have dreams? If people did not strive for what they

believe in? We must have dreams. We must have ideals. We must fight for things we believe in. We must believe in ourselves. But there are also realities we must face. We can only attempt to make the best of any given situation or circumstances. If we are not successful, we must not give up hope. We must tell ourselves that we can only try a little harder the next time.

Over the past few years, in my visits to Inuit communities, I have had many private conversations about what is happening to our people and what the future holds for us. I have become more and more concerned about the angry words which some of our people are starting to use. I cannot really blame them for their feelings. Their feelings towards white people are easy to understand. It is very easy to blame white people for the predicament we find ourselves in today. But anger and hate are not the answers. We need the patience and understanding of our white brothers and sisters. If we are to expect that from them, we must offer the same in return. The Inuit, by nature, are not violent people. This is one of our virtues which we must not lose.

It disturbs me a great deal to hear about native organizations squabbling with other native organizations. If we are to achieve anything, we must not fight among ourselves. We can agree to disagree, but we must sort out our problems together. We must be of one mind and of one voice. This is not always possible among human beings. But we must not let petty disagreements divide us.

The Inuit were once strong, independent and proud people. That is why we have survived. That strength, that independence, and that pride must surface again. We must prove to Canada that the original citizens of this country will not lie down and play dead. After all, the Inuit have been described by the United Nations as a people who refuse to disappear.

Kiawak Ashoona *Smiling Family* 1966

Borders

◆ ◆ ◆

BY

THOMAS

KING

When I was twelve, maybe thirteen, my mother announced that we were going to go to Salt Lake City to visit my sister who had left the reserve, moved across the line, and found a job. Laetitia had not left home with my mother's blessing, but over time my mother had come to be proud of the fact that Laetitia had done all of this on her own.

"She did real good," my mother would say.

Then there were the fine points to Laetitia's going. She had not, as my mother liked to tell Mrs. Manyfingers, gone floating after some man like a balloon on a string. She hadn't snuck out of the house, either, and gone to Vancouver or Edmonton or Toronto to chase rainbows down alleys. And she hadn't been pregnant.

"She did real good."

I was seven or eight when Laetitia left home. She was seventeen. Our father was from Rocky Boy on the American side.

"Dad's American," Laetitia told my mother, "so I can go and come as I please."

"Send us a postcard."

Laetitia packed her things, and we headed for the border. Just outside of Milk River, Laetitia told us to watch for the water tower.

"Over the next rise. It's the first thing you see."

"We got a water tower on the reserve," my mother said. "There's a big one in Lethbridge, too."

"You'll be able to see the tops of the flagpoles, too. That's where the border is."

When we got to Coutts, my mother stopped at the convenience store and bought her and Laetitia a cup of coffee. I got an Orange Crush.

"This is real lousy coffee."

"You're just angry because I want to see the world."

"It's the water. From here on down, they got lousy water."

"I can catch the bus from Sweetgrass. You don't have to lift a finger."

"You're going to have to buy your water in bottles if you want good coffee."

There was an old wooden building about a block away, with a tall sign in the yard that said "Museum." Most of the roof had been blown away. Mom told me to go and see when the place was open. There were boards over the windows and doors. You could tell that the place was closed, and I told Mom so, but she said to go and check anyway. Mom and Laetitia stayed by the car. Neither one of them moved. I sat down on the steps of the museum and watched them, and I don't know that they ever said anything to each other. Finally, Laetitia got her bag out of the trunk and gave Mom a hug.

I wandered back to the car. The wind had come up, and it blew Laetitia's hair across her face. Mom reached out and pulled the strands out of Laetitia's eyes, and Laetitia let her.

"You can still see the mountain from here," my mother told Laetitia in Blackfoot.

"Lots of mountains in Salt Lake," Laetitia told her in English.

"The place is closed," I said. "Just like I told you."

Laetitia tucked her hair into her jacket and dragged her bag down the road to the brick building with the American flag flapping on a pole. When she got to where the guards were waiting, she turned, put the bag down, and waved to us. We waved back. Then my mother turned the car around, and we came home.

We got postcards from Laetitia regular, and, if she wasn't spreading jelly on the truth, she was happy. She found a good job and rented an apartment with a pool.

"And she can't even swim," my mother told Mrs. Manyfingers.

Most of the postcards said we should come down and see the city, but whenever I mentioned this, my mother would stiffen up.

So I was surprised when she bought two new tires for the car and put on her blue dress with the green and yellow flowers. I had to dress up, too, for my mother did not want us crossing the border looking like Americans. We made sandwiches and put them in a big box with pop and potato chips and some apples and bananas and a big jar of water.

"But we can stop at one of those restaurants, too, right?"

"We maybe should take some blankets in case you get sleepy."

"But we can stop at one of those restaurants, too, right?"

The border was actually two towns, though neither one was big enough to amount to anything. Coutts was on the Canadian side and consisted of the convenience store and gas station, the museum that was closed and boarded up, and a motel. Sweetgrass was on the American side, but all you could see was an overpass that arched across the highway and disappeared into the prairies. Just hearing the names of these towns, you would expect that Sweetgrass, which is a nice name and sounds like it is related to other places such as Medicine Hat and Moose Jaw and Kicking Horse Pass, would be on the Canadian side and that Coutts, which sounds abrupt and rude, would be on the American side. But this was not the case.

Between the two borders was a duty-free shop where you could buy cigarettes and liquor and flags. Stuff like that.

We left the reserve in the morning and drove until we got to Coutts.

"Last time we stopped here," my mother said, "you had an Orange Crush. You remember that?"

"Sure," I said. "That was when Laetitia took off."

"You want another Orange Crush?"

"That means we're not going to stop at a restaurant, right?"

My mother got a coffee at the convenience store, and we stood around and watched the prairies move in the sunlight. Then we climbed back in the car. My mother straightened the dress across her thighs, leaned against the wheel, and drove all the way to the border in first gear, slowly, as if she were trying to see through a bad storm or riding high on black ice.

The border guard was an old guy. As he walked to the car, he swayed from side to side, his feet set wide apart, the holster on his hip pitching up and down. He leaned into the window, looking into the back seat, and looked at my mother and me.

"Morning, ma'am."

"Good morning."

"Where are you heading?"

"Salt Lake City."

"Purpose of your visit?"

"Visit my daughter."

"Citizenship?"

"Blackfoot," my mother told him.

"Ma'am?"

"Blackfoot," my mother repeated.

"Canadian?"

"Blackfoot."

It would have been easier if my mother had just said "Canadian" and been done with it, but I could see she wasn't going to do that. The guard wasn't angry or anything. He smiled and looked towards the building. Then he turned back and nodded.

"Morning, ma'am."

"Good morning."

"Any firearms or tobacco?"

"No."

"Citizenship?"

"Blackfoot."

He told us to sit in the car and wait, and we did. In about five minutes, another guard came out with the first man. They were talking as they came, both men swaying back and forth like two cowboys headed for a bar or a gunfight.

"Morning, ma'am."

"Good morning."

"Cecil tells me you and the boy are Blackfoot."

"That's right."

"Now, I know that we got Blackfeet on the American side and the Canadians got Blackfeet on their side. Just so we can keep our records straight, what side do you come from?"

I knew exactly what my mother was going to say, and I could have told them if they had asked me.

"Canadian side or American side?" asked the guard.

"Blackfoot side," she said.

It didn't take them long to lose their sense of humour, I can tell you that. The one guard stopped smiling altogether and told us to park our car at the side of the building and come in.

We sat on a wood bench for about an hour before anyone came over to talk to us. This time it was a woman. She had a gun, too.

"Hi," she said. "I'm Inspector Pratt. I understand there is a little misunderstanding."

"I'm going to visit my daughter in Salt Lake City," my mother told her. "We don't have any guns or beer."

"It's a legal technicality, that's all."

"My daughter's Blackfoot, too."

The woman opened a briefcase and took out a couple of forms and began to write on one of them. "Everyone who crosses our border has to declare their citizenship. Even Americans. It helps us keep track of the visitors we get from the various countries."

She went on like that for maybe fifteen minutes, and a lot of the stuff she told us was interesting.

"I can understand how you feel about having to tell us your citizenship, and here's what I'll do. You tell me, and I won't put it down on the form. No-one will know but you and me."

Her gun was silver. There were several chips in the wood handle and the name "Stella" was scratched into the metal butt.

We were in the border office for about four hours, and we talked to almost everyone there. One of the men bought me a Coke. My mother brought a couple of sandwiches in from the car. I offered part of mine to Stella, but she said she wasn't hungry.

I told Stella that we were Blackfoot and Canadian, but she said that that didn't count because I was a minor. In the end, she told us that if my mother didn't declare her citizenship, we would have to go back to where we came from. My mother stood up and thanked Stella for her time. Then we got back in the car and drove to the Canadian border, which was only about a hundred yards away.

I was disappointed. I hadn't seen Laetitia for a long time, and I had never been to Salt Lake City. When she was still at home, Laetitia would go on and on about Salt Lake City. She had never been there, but her boyfriend Lester Tallbull had spent a year in Salt Lake at a technical school.

"It's a great place," Lester would say. "Nothing but blondes in the whole state."

Whenever he said that, Laetitia would slug him on his shoulder hard enough to make him flinch. He had some brochures on Salt Lake and some maps, and every so often the two of them would spread them out on the table.

"That's the temple. It's right downtown. You got to have a pass to get in."

"Charlotte says anyone can go in and look around."

"When was Charlotte in Salt Lake? Just when the hell was Charlotte in Salt Lake?"

"Last year."

"This is Liberty Park. It's got a zoo. There's good skiing in the mountains."

"Got all the skiing we can use," my mother would say. "People come from all over the world to ski at Banff. Cardston's got a temple, if you like those kind of things."

"Oh, this one is real big," Lester would say. "They got armed guards and everything."

"Not what Charlotte says."

"What does she know?"

Lester and Laetitia broke up, but I guess the idea of Salt Lake stuck in her mind.

The Canadian border guard was a young woman, and she seemed happy to see us. "Hi," she said. "You folks sure have a great day for a trp. Where are you coming from?"

"Standoff."

"Is that in Montana?"

"No."

"Where are you going?"

"Standoff."

The woman's name was Carol and I don't guess she was any older than Laetitia. "Wow, you both Canadians?"

"Blackfoot."

"Really? I have a friend I went to school with who is Blackfoot. Do you know Mike Harley?"

"No."

"He went to school in Lethbridge, but he's really from Browning."

It was a nice conversation and there were no cars behind us, so there was no rush.

"You're not bringing any liquor back, are you?"

"No."

"Any cigarettes or plants or stuff like that?"

"No."

"Citizenship?"

"Blackfoot."

"I know," said the woman, "and I'd be proud of being Blackfoot if I were Blackfoot. But you have to be American or Canadian."

When Laetitia and Lester broke up, Lester took his brochures and maps with him, so Laetitia wrote to someone in Salt Lake City, and, about a month later, she got a big envelope of stuff. We sat at the table and opened up all the brochures, and Laetitia read each one out loud.

"Salt Lake City is the gateway to some of the world's most magnificent skiing."

"Salt Lake City is the home of one of the newest professional basketball franchises, the Utah Jazz.

"The Great Salt Lake is one of the natural wonders of the world."

It was kind of exciting seeing all those colour brochures on the table and listening to Laetitia read all about how Salt Lake City was one of the best places in the entire world.

"That Salt Lake City place sounds too good to be true," my mother told her.

"It has everything."

"We got everything right here."

"It's boring here."

"People in Salt Lake City are probably sending away for brochures of Calgary and Lethbridge and Pincher Creek right now."

In the end, my mother would say that maybe Laetitia should go to Salt Lake City, and Laetitia would say that maybe she would.

We parked the car to the side of the building and Carol led us into a small room on the second floor. I found a comfortable spot on the couch and flipped through some back issues of *Saturday Night* and *Alberta Report*.

When I woke up, my mother was just coming out of another office. She didn't say a word to me. I followed her down the stairs and out to the car. I thought we were going home, but she turned the car around and drove back towards the American border, which made me think we were going to visit Laetitia in Salt Lake City after all. Instead she pulled into the parking lot of the duty-free store and stopped.

"We going to see Laetitia?"

"No."

"We going home?"

Pride is a good thing to have, you know. Laetitia had a lot of pride, and so did my mother. I figured that someday, I'd have it, too.

"So where are we going?"

Most of that day, we wandered around the duty-free store, which wasn't very large. The manager had a name tag with a tiny American flag on one side and a tiny Canadian flag on the other. His name was Mel. Towards evening, he began suggesting that we should be on our way. I told him we had nowhere to go, that neither the Americans nor the Canadians would let us in. He laughed at that and told us that we should buy something or leave.

The car was not very comfortable, but we did have all that food and it was April, so even if it did snow as it sometimes does on the prairies, we wouldn't freeze. The next morning my mother drove to the American border.

It was a different guard this time, but the questions were the same. We didn't spend as much time in the office as we had the day before. By noon, we were back at the Canadian border. By two we were back in the duty-free shop parking lot.

The second night in the car was not as much fun as the first, but my mother seemed in good spirits, and, all in all, it was as much an adventure as an inconvenience. There wasn't much food left and that was a problem, but we had lots of water as there was a faucet at the side of the duty-free shop.

One Sunday, Laetitia and I were watching television. Mom was over at Mrs. Manyfingers's. Right in the middle of the programme, Laetitia turned off the set and said she was going to Salt Lake City, that life around here was too boring. I had wanted to see the rest of the programme and really didn't care if Laetitia went to Salt Lake City or not. When Mom got home, I told her what Laetitia had said.

What surprised me was how angry Laetitia got when she found out that I had told Mom.

"You got a big mouth."

"That's what you said."

"What I said is none of your business."

"I didn't say anything."

"Well, I'm going for sure, now."

That weekend, Laetitia packed her bags, and we drove her to the border.

Mel turned out to be friendly. When he closed up for the night and found us still parked in the lot, he came over and asked us if our car was broken down or something. My mother thanked him for his concern and told him that we were fine, that things would get straightened out in the morning.

"You're kidding," said Mel. "You'd think they could handle the simple things."

"We got some apples and a banana," I said, "but we're all out of ham sandwiches."

"You know, you read about these things, but you just don't believe it. You just don't believe it."

"Hamburgers would be even better because they got more stuff for energy."

My mother slept in the back seat. I slept in the front because I was smaller and could lie under the steering wheel. Late that night, I heard my mother open the car door. I found her sitting on her blanket leaning against the bumper of the car.

"You see all those stars," she said. "When I was a little girl, my grandmother used to take me and my sisters out on the prairies and tell us stories about all the stars."

"Do you think Mel is going to bring us any hamburgers?"

"Every one of those stars has a story. You see that bunch of stars over there that look like a fish?"

"He didn't say no."

"Coyote went fishing, one day. That's how it all started." We sat out under the stars that night, and my mother told me all sorts of stories. She was serious about it, too. She'd tell them slow, repeating parts as she went, as if she expected me to remember each other.

Early the next morning the television vans began to arrive, and guys in suits and women in dresses came trotting over to us, dragging microphones and cameras and lights behind them. One of the vans had a table set up with orange juice and sandwiches and fruit. It was for the crew, but when I told them we hadn't eaten for a while, a really skinny blonde woman told us we could eat as much as we wanted.

They mostly talked to my mother. Every so often one of the reporters would come over and ask me questions about how it felt to be an Indian without a country. I told them we had a nice house on the reserve and that my cousins had a couple of horses we rode when we went fishing. Some of the television people went over to the American border, and then they went to the Canadian border.

Around noon, a good-looking guy in a dark blue suit and an orange tie with little ducks on it drove up in a fancy car. He talked to my mother for a while, and, after they were done talking, my mother called me over, and we got into our car. Just as my mother started the engine, Mel came over and gave us a bag of peanut brittle and told us that justice was a damn hard thing to get, but that we shouldn't give up.

I would have preferred lemon drops, but it was nice of Mel anyway.

"Where are we going now?"

"Going to visit Laetitia."

The guard who came out to our car was all smiles. The television lights were so bright they hurt my eyes, and, if you tried to look through the windshield in certain directions, you couldn't see a thing.

"Morning, ma'am."

"Good morning."

"Where are you heading?"

"Salt Lake City."

"Purpose of your visit?"

"Visit my daughter."

"Any tobacco, liquor, or firearms?"

"Don't smoke."

"Any plants or fruit?"

"Not any more."

"Citizenship?"

"Blackfoot."

The guard rocked back on his heels and jammed his thumbs into his gun belt. "Thank you," he said, his fingers patting the butt of the revolver. "Have a pleasant trip."

My mother rolled the car forward, and the television people had to scramble out of the way. They ran alongside the car as we pulled away from the border, and, when they couldn't run any farther, they stood in the middle of the highway and waved and waved and waved.

We got to Salt Lake City the next day. Laetitia was happy to see us, and, that first night, she took us out to a restaurant that made really good soups. The list of pies took up a whole page. I had cherry. Mom had chocolate. Laetitia said that she saw us on television the night before and, during the meal, she had us tell her the story over and over again.

Laetitia took us everywhere. We went to a fancy ski resort. We went to the temple. We got to go shopping in a couple of large malls, but they weren't as large as the one in Edmonton, and Mom said so.

After a week or so, I got bored and wasn't at all sad when my mother said we should be heading back home. Laetitia wanted us to stay longer, but Mom said no, that she had things to do back home and that, next time, Laetitia should come up and visit. Laetitia said she was thinking about moving back, and Mom told her to do as she pleased, and Laetitia said that she would.

On the way home, we stopped at the duty-free shop, and my mother gave Mel a green hat that said "Salt Lake" across the front. Mel was a funny guy. He took the hat and blew his nose and told my mother that she was an inspiration to us all. He gave us some more peanut brittle and came out into the parking lot and waved at us all the way to the Canadian border.

It was almost evening when we left Coutts. I watched the border through the rear window until all you could see were the tops of the flagpoles and the blue water tower, and then they rolled over a hill and disappeared.

Jamaican Fragment

♦ ♦ ♦

BY A. L. HENDRICKS

Every day I walk a half-mile from my home to the tramcar lines in the morning, and from the lines to my home in the evening. The walk is pleasant. The road on either side is flanked by red- and green-roofed bungalows, green lawns and gardens. The exercise is good for me and now and then I learn something from a little incident.

One morning, about half-way between my front gate and the tram track, I noticed two little boys playing in the garden of one of the more modest cottages. They were both very little boys, one was four years old perhaps, the other five. The bigger of the two was a sturdy young-ster, very dark, with a mat of coarse hair on his head and coal-black eyes. He was definitely a little Jamaican — a strong little Jamaican. The other little fellow was smaller, but also sturdy — he was white, with hazel eyes and light-brown hair. Both were dressed in blue shirts and khaki pants: they wore no shoes and their feet were muddy. They were not conscious of my standing there watching them; they played on. The game, if it could be called a game, was not elaborate. The little white boy strode imperiously up and down and every now and then shouted imperiously at his bigger playmate. The little brown boy shuf-fled along quietly behind him and did what he was told.

"Pick up that stick!" The dark boy picked it up.

"Jump into the flowers!" The dark boy jumped.

"Get me some water!" The dark boy ran inside. The white boy sat down on the lawn.

I was amazed. Here before my eyes, a white baby, for they were little more than babies, was imposing his will upon a little black boy. And the little black boy submitted. I puzzled within myself as I went down the road. Could it be that the little dark boy was the son of a servant in the home and therefore had to do the white boy's bidding? No. They were obviously dressed alike, the little dark boy was of equal class with his playmate. No. They were playmates, the little dark boy was a neighbour's child. I was sure of that. Then how was it that he obeyed so faithfully the white boy's orders? Was it that even at his early age he sensed that in his own country he would be at the white man's beck and call? Could he in such youth divine a difference between himself and the white boy? And did the little white youngster so young, such a baby, realize that he would grow to dominate the black man? Was there an indefinable quality in the white man that enabled his baby, smaller and younger than his playmate, to make him his slave? Was there really some difference between a white man and a black man? Something that made the white superior? I could find no answer. I could not bring myself to believe such a thing, and yet, with my own eyes I had seen a little dark boy take orders from a little white boy — a little white boy obviously his social equal, and younger and smaller. Were we as a race really inferior? So inferior that even in our infancy we realized our deficiencies, and accept a position as the white man's servant?

For a whole day I puzzled over this problem. For a whole day my faith in my people was shaken. When I passed that afternoon the little boys were not there. That evening I thought deeply on the subject.

The next morning the boys were there again, and a man was standing at the gate watching them. I stopped and looked, just to see what the white boy was making his little servant do. To my utter astonishment the little dark boy was striding imperiously up and down the lawn, while the white youngster walked abjectly behind him.

"Get me a banana!" The little white boy ran into the house and reappeared shortly with a banana. "Peel it for me!" The little white boy skinned the banana and handed it to his dark master.

I saw it now. This was indeed a game, a game I had played as a child. Each boy took it in turn every alternate day to be the boss, the other the slave. It had been great fun to me as a youngster. I smiled as I remembered. I looked at the man standing by the gate. He was a white man. I remembered what I had thought yesterday. He, no doubt, I thought to myself, was wondering if the black race is superior to the white. I laughed gently to myself. How silly grown-ups are, how clever we are, how wonderfully able we are to impute deep motives to childish actions! How suspicious we are when we have been warped by prejudice! This man, I said to myself, will puzzle all day on whether the blacks will eventually arise and rule the world because he thinks he sees a little black boy realizing at a tender age his superiority over the white. I will save him his puzzle. I will explain it to him. I went across to him.

"I know what you're thinking," I said. "You're thinking that maybe the black race is superior to the white, because you just saw the little dark youngster on the lawn ordering the little white boy around. Don't think that, it's a game they play. Alternate days one is boss, the other the servant. It's a grand game. I used to play it and maybe so did you. Yesterday I saw the little white boy bossing the dark one and I worried all day over the dark boy's realization of his inferiority so young in life! We are silly, we grown-ups, aren't we?"

The man was surprised at my outburst. He looked at me smiling.

"I know all about the game," he said. "The boys are brothers—my sons." He pointed to a handsome brown woman on the veranda who had just come out to call in the children. "That's my wife," he said.

I smiled. My spirit laughed within me. This is Jamaica, I said in my heart, this is my country—my people. I looked at the white man. He smiled at me. "We'll miss the tram if we don't hurry," he said.

ACKNOWLEDGEMENTS

Care has been taken to trace ownership of copyright material contained in this text. The publishers will gladly accept any information that will enable them to rectify any reference or credit in subsequent editions.

TEXT

p. 1 "A Multicultural Nation" by Winston Loui. From *New Canadian Voices* edited by Jessie Porter. Reprinted with the permission of the publisher, Wall & Emerson, Inc., Toronto; **p. 2** "Wall" by Adam Kozakiewicz. Reprinted by permission of Adam Kozakiewicz; **p. 5** "Smile" by Kit Wong. From *New Canadian Voices* edited by Jessie Porter. Reprinted with the permission of the publisher, Wall & Emerson, Inc., Toronto; **p. 10** "I am a Canadian" by Duke Redbird. Reprinted by permission of Duke Redbird; **p. 12** "The Profile of Africa" by Maxine Tynes. Originally published in *Borrowed Beauty*, 1987, and now appearing in *Save the World For Me*, 1991, Pottersfield Press; **p. 14** "Palumello" by Donna Caruso. Reprinted from *Out of Place*, Coteau Books, Sask. Originally written for CBC Radio entitled "Lullaby"; **p. 27** "Tara's Mother-in-law" by Uma Parameswaran. Reprinted by permission of the publisher. From *Trishanku* by Uma Parameswaran (Toronto: TSAR, 1988); **p. 29** "The Evening I Met My Grandmother, April 20, 1987" by Gita Schwartz. Reprinted from *Fireweed: A Feminist Quarterly: Jewish Women, Spring 1992*; **p. 32** "The Jade Peony" by Wayson Choy, first published in the *UBC Alumni Chronicle*, copyright © 1979 by Wayson Choy; **p. 41** "I Grew Up" by Lenore Keeshig-Tobias. From *Seventh Generation* edited by Heather Hodgson, 1989. Originally published by Theytus Books; **p. 43** "What Do We Do with a Variation?" by James Berry from *When I Dance*. Copyright © James Berry, 1988. Published by Hamish Hamilton Children's Books, 1988. Reproduced by permission of Hamish Hamilton Ltd.; **p. 45** "The Other Family" by Himani Bannerji. Reprinted by permission of the author; **p. 50** "Should I Change My Name?" by Matheyalagan Nagaranthy. From *New Canadian Voices* edited by Jessie Porter. Reprinted with the permission of the publisher, Wall & Emerson, Inc., Toronto; **p. 51** "The Nun Who Returned to Ireland" by Roch Carrier. From *The Hockey Sweater and Other Stories* by Roch Carrier published by The House of Anansi Press. Reprinted by permission of Stoddart Publishing Company Limited; **p. 54** "Our Subdivision" by Nigel Darbasie. Reprinted from *Last Crossing* by permission of Nidar Communications Inc. Copyright © 1988 by Nigel Darbasie; **p. 55** "Equal Opportunity" by Jim Wong-Chu. Reprinted with permission from *East of Main: An Anthology of Poems from East Vancouver*, edited by Calvin Wharton and Tom Wayman (Arsenal Pulp Press, 1989); **p. 58** "Meeting Jim Crow" by Cheryl Foggo. Permission to reprint this material was granted by Detselig Enterprises Ltd., Calgary, Alberta; **p. 65** excerpt from *Angel Square* by Brian Doyle. Copyright © 1984 by Brian Doyle. A Groundwood Book/Douglas & McIntyre; **p. 67** "The Second Day" (chapter 11) from *From Anna* by Jean Little. Copyright © 1972 by Jean Little. Selection reprinted by permission of HarperCollins Publishers; **p. 79** "A Child in Prison Camp" by Shizuye Takashima. Taken from *A Child in Prison Camp*, © 1971 Shizuye Takashima, published by Tundra Books; **p. 87** "Acknowledgement" reproduced with the permission of Multiculturalism and Citizenship Canada and © the Minister of Supply and Services Canada, 1992; **p. 88** "Kanadalainen" by Nancy Mattson originally appeared in *Maria Breaks Her Silence* by Nancy Mattson (Coteau Books, 1989). Reprinted with the permission of the publisher; **p. 90** "Immigrants: The Second Generation" by Kevin Irie from *Relations: Family Portraits* edited by Kenneth Sherman © 1986, Mosaic Press, Oakville, Ontario, L6L 5N9. Reprinted with permission of the publisher; **p. 92** "I Want My Chaos Back" by Surjeet Kalsey was first published in *Footprints of Silence*, 1988, Third Eye Publications, London, Ontario; **p. 93** "Why My Mother Can't Speak English" by Garry Engkent. Reprinted by permission of the author; **p. 100** "Heritage Day" from *Deep North* by Bert Almon (Thistledown Press Ltd., 1984) used with permission; **p. 102** "Refugee" by M.G. Vassanji. From *Uhuru Street* by M.G. Vassanji. Used by permission of the Canadian Publishers, McClelland & Stewart, Toronto; **p. 113** "Illegals: Shadows in the Underground" by Marina Jiminez and Corinna Schuler. Reprinted with permission of *The Edmonton Journal*; **p. 117** "Beyond the Sea" by Nick Lees. Reprinted with permission of *The Edmonton Journal*; **p. 121** "Involvement Overcomes Isolation" by Lesley Francis. Reprinted with permission of *The Edmonton Journal*; **p. 125** "Points 26, 27, 28 of Canada's original Immigration Act." From the Department of Justice Canada. Reproduced with the permission of the Queen's Printer for Canada, 1992; **p. 127** from the Multiculturalism Policy of Canada. Reproduced with the permission of Multiculturalism and Citizenship Canada and © the Minister of Supply and Services, Canada, 1993; **p. 129** "Youth Our Best Hope to End Racial Discrimination" by Gerry Weiner. Reprinted by permission of The Honourable Gerry Weiner, Minister of Multiculturalism and Citizenship; **p. 133** "We Must Have Dreams" by John Amagoalik. Reprinted with the permission of the Inuit Tapirisat of Canada; **p. 136** "Borders" by Thomas King copyright © 1991 by Thomas King. Used by permission.

PHOTOGRAPHS

p. 4 Jim Wunnenberg; **p. 13** UNICEF/Giacomo Pirozzi; **p. 19** World Wildlife Fund/Steven Price; **p. 24** National Archives of Canada, C-5611/John Woodruff; **p. 31** Canadian Jewish Congress National Archives PC1-1-4G; **p. 40** E. Jane Mundy; **p. 44** Bill Ivy; **p. 57** Provincial Archives, Victoria, B.C. BCARS HP 54020; **p. 64** Ministry of Citizenship and Culture; **p. 78** Vancouver Public Library 14925 **p. 86** Vancouver Public Library 1392; **p. 99** Canada Wide Feature Service Ltd./Barry Gray; **p. 101** UNICEF/Jean Mohr; **p. 112** and **p. 114** Canapress Photo Service; **p. 119** *The Edmonton Journal*/John Lucas; **p. 123** *The Edmonton Journal*/Sean Connor; **p. 128** World Wildlife Fund; **p. 135** Kiawak Ashoona 1933- Cape Dorset *Smiling Family* 1966, green stone 32.5 x 48.5 x 17.5 cm, McMichael Canadian Art Collection, Gift of the Founders, Robert and Signe McMichael 1975. 69. 2.